Contents

Introduction

The contents of this book are based upon the National Science Education Standards for Grade 6. These standards include (A) Science as Inquiry, (B) Physical Science, (C) Life Science, (D) Earth and Space Science, (E) Science and Technology, (F) Science in Personal and Social Perspectives, and (G) History and Nature of Science.

This book will help teachers, students, parents, and tutors. Teachers can use this book either to introduce or review a topic in their science classroom. Students will find the book useful in reviewing the major concepts in science. Parents can use this book to help their children with topics that may be posing a problem in the classroom. Tutors can use this book as a basis for their lessons and for assigning questions and activities.

This book includes ten lessons that focus on the ten major concepts presented in the content standards: Physical Science, Life Science, and Earth and Space Science. The lessons also cover the twelve major concepts presented in the other standards. A table on page 4 provides a correlation between the contents of each lesson and the National Science Education Standards.

Before beginning the book, the reader can check his or her knowledge of the content by completing the *Assessment*. The *Assessment* consists of questions that deal with the content standards. This will allow the reader to determine how much he or she knows about a particular concept before beginning to read about it. The *Assessment* may also serve as a way of leading the reader to a specific lesson that may be of special interest.

Each lesson follows the same sequence in presenting the material. A list of *Key Terms* is always provided at the beginning of each lesson. This list includes all the boldfaced terms and their definitions presented in the same order that they are introduced in the lesson. The reader can develop a sense of the lesson content by glancing through the *Key Terms*. Each lesson then provides background information about the concept. This information is divided into several sections. Each section is written so that the reader is not overwhelmed with details. Rather, the reader is guided through the concept in a logical sequence. Each lesson then moves on to a *Review*. This section consists of several multiple-choice and short-answer questions. The multiple-choice questions check if the reader has retained information that was covered in the lesson. The short-answer questions check if the reader can use information from the lesson to provide the answers.

Each lesson then moves on to a series of activities. These activities are designed to check the reader's understanding of the information. Some activities extend the lesson by presenting additional information. The activities are varied so as not to be boring. For example, reading passages about interesting and unusual findings are included. Questions to check reading comprehension are then asked. As a change of pace, some activities are meant to engage the reader in a "fun-type" exercise. These activities include crosswords, word searches, jumbled letters, and cryptograms.

The last activity in each lesson is an experiment. Each experiment has been designed so that the required items are easy to locate and can usually be found in most households. Care has been taken to avoid the use of any dangerous materials or chemicals. However, an adult should always be present when a student is conducting an experiment. In some cases, the experimental procedure reminds students that adult supervision is required. Before beginning any experiment, an adult should review the list of materials and the procedure. In this way, the adult will be aware of any situations that may need special attention. The adult should review the safety issues before the experiment is begun. The adult may want to check a laboratory manual for specific safety precautions that should be followed when doing an experiment, such as wearing safety goggles and never touching or tasting chemicals.

The book then follows with a *Science Fair* section. Information is presented on how to conduct and present a science fair project. In some cases, the experiment at the end of a lesson can serve as the basis for a science fair project. Additional suggestions are also provided with advice on how to choose an award-winning science fair project.

A *Glossary* is next. This section lists all the boldfaced terms in alphabetical order and indicates the page on which the term is used. The book concludes with an *Answer Key*, which gives the answers to all the activity questions, including the experiment.

This book has been designed and written so that teachers, students, parents, and tutors will find it easy to use and follow. Most importantly, students will benefit from this book by achieving at a higher level in class and on standardized tests.

National Science Education Standards

Standard A: SCIENCE AS INQUIRY
A1 Abilities necessary to do scientific inquiry
A2 Understandings about scientific inquiry

Standard B: PHYSICAL SCIENCE
B1 Properties and changes of properties in matter
B2 Motions and forces
B3 Transfer of energy

Standard C: LIFE SCIENCE
C1 Structure and function in living systems
C2 Reproduction and heredity
C3 Regulation and behavior
C4 Populations and ecosystems
C5 Diversity and adaptations of organisms

Standard D: EARTH AND SPACE SCIENCE
D1 Earth's history and structure
D2 Earth in the solar system

Standard E: SCIENCE AND TECHNOLOGY
E1 Abilities of technological design
E2 Understandings about science and technology

Standard F: SCIENCE IN PERSONAL AND SOCIAL PERSPECTIVES
F1 Personal health
F2 Populations, resources, and environments
F3 Natural hazards
F4 Risks and benefits
F5 Science and technology in society

Standard G: HISTORY AND NATURE OF SCIENCE
G1 Science as a human endeavor
G2 Nature of science
G3 History of science

Correlation to National Science Education Standards

Assessment

Darken the circle by the best answer.

1. A chemical change occurs
   - (A) whenever new substances are produced.
   - (B) when a piece of paper is torn in half.
   - (C) if the density of a substance is measured.
   - (D) when a substance melts.

2. An object is being pushed upward by a force of 20 N. The object is also being pulled downward by a force of 5 N. The net force on this object is
   - (A) 5 N.
   - (B) 10 N.
   - (C) 15 N.
   - (D) 25 N.

3. You can feel the warmth from the sun on your skin. How is heat transferred from the sun to you?
   - (A) conduction
   - (B) convection
   - (C) radiation
   - (D) current

4. Which of the following statements about a series circuit is true?
   - (A) A series circuit does not contain any loads.
   - (B) Electrons flow in only a single path.
   - (C) The failure of one load does not affect another load.
   - (D) No electrons flow through the circuit.

5. What function does a cell membrane perform?
   - (A) digesting food materials and harmful particles
   - (B) producing proteins
   - (C) packaging proteins
   - (D) controlling what enters and leaves the cell

6. If an immature sex cell contains 24 chromosomes, how many chromosomes are present in a mature sex cell?
   - (A) 8
   - (B) 12
   - (C) 24
   - (D) 48

7. The maintenance of a stable internal environment despite changes in the external environment is called
   - (A) diffusion.
   - (B) osmosis.
   - (C) endocytosis.
   - (D) homeostasis.

8. The process in which water moves from an area of high concentration to an area of low concentration is called
   - (A) capillary action.
   - (B) osmosis.
   - (C) exocytosis.
   - (D) active transport.

Assessment, page 2

9. If one organism benefits while the other organism is not affected, then this relationship is known as

Ⓐ mutualism.

Ⓑ commensalism.

Ⓒ competition.

Ⓓ parasitism.

10. The role an organism plays in its environment is known as its

Ⓐ habitat.

Ⓑ community.

Ⓒ niche.

Ⓓ social status.

11. Which part of an organism is most likely to become a fossil?

Ⓐ muscle

Ⓑ skull

Ⓒ stomach

Ⓓ brain

12. The half-life of an unstable atom is 500 years. If a sample contains 10 grams of this unstable atom, what percentage of the original sample will be left after 1,000 years?

Ⓐ 100%   Ⓒ 50%

Ⓑ 75%   Ⓓ 25%

13. Magma is

Ⓐ hot, liquid rock.

Ⓑ weathered rock.

Ⓒ igneous rock.

Ⓓ the top layer of soil.

14. Which process is part of the rock cycle?

Ⓐ diffusion

Ⓑ radioactive decay

Ⓒ weathering

Ⓓ respiration

15. Which planet is classified as a gas giant?

Ⓐ Earth

Ⓑ Mars

Ⓒ Jupiter

Ⓓ Venus

16. If a planet has a retrograde rotation, then this planet

Ⓐ orbits the sun very slowly.

Ⓑ orbits the sun once every 365 days.

Ⓒ spins in a counterclockwise direction as seen from above its North Pole.

Ⓓ spins in a clockwise direction as seen from above its North Pole.

Lesson 1 Properties and Changes of Properties in Matter

A star in a distant galaxy, this book, and you all have something in common. In fact, everything in the universe has something in common. Everything that you can see is made of matter. **Matter** is anything that has both volume and mass. **Volume** is the amount of space that is taken up, or occupied, by an object.

For example, the volume of this book is the amount of space it takes up on a bookshelf or in your backpack. **Mass** is the amount of matter in an object. Because it has more pages, the mass of a dictionary is greater than the mass of this book. In this lesson, you will learn more about matter.

Key Terms

matter—anything that has both volume and mass

volume—the amount of space taken up, or occupied, by an object

mass—the amount of matter in an object

physical property—property that can be observed or measured without changing the matter's identity

weight—a measure of the force of gravity on the mass of an object

chemical property—a property that allows matter to be changed into new matter that has different properties

physical change—a change that affects one or more physical properties of an object

chemical change—a change that occurs when one or more substances are changed into new substances that have different properties

chemical reaction—a process in which one or more substances change to make one or more new substances

reactant—a starting material in a chemical reaction

product—a substance that is formed in a chemical reaction

chemical equation—a way to represent a chemical reaction using chemical symbols and numbers

chemical formula—a combination of chemical symbols and numbers to represent a substance

synthesis reaction—a reaction in which two or more reactants combine to form one product

decomposition reaction—a reaction in which a single reactant breaks down to form two or more products

Properties of Matter

Both volume and mass are examples of physical properties of matter. A **physical property** of matter can be observed or measured without changing the matter's identity. You can determine the volume of this book by measuring its length, width, and height. If you multiply these three values, you will get the volume of this book.

You can determine the mass of this book by using a balance.

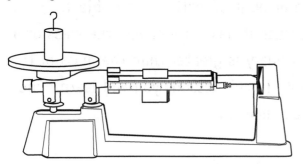

Mass is not the same as weight. **Weight** is a measure of the force of gravity on the mass of an object. The mass of an object is always the same no matter where the object is located in the universe. In contrast, the weight of an object depends on where the object is located. For example, an object will weigh much less on the moon where the force of gravity is less than it is on Earth.

Notice that you do not change the identity of this book by determining its volume and mass. As a result, volume and mass are physical properties of matter. Other physical properties of matter include color, boiling point, melting point, and attraction to magnets.

Matter also has chemical properties. A **chemical property** is a property that allows matter to be changed into new matter that has different properties. For example, wood can be burned to produce smoke and ashes. The smoke and ashes are new substances that have very different properties than the wood.

Therefore, flammability, or the ability to burn, is a chemical property of wood.

Unlike physical properties, chemical properties are not so easy to observe or measure. You can easily measure the volume and mass of this book. However, you cannot tell that flammability is a chemical property unless the wood is burning. Even so, flammability is still a chemical property of wood even though it is not burning.

Changes in Properties

You can remove pages from this book. If you do, then you have changed one of its physical properties. Removing pages from this book is an example of a physical change. A **physical change** is a change that affects one or more physical properties of an object. After pages have been removed, the book will no longer have the same volume and mass as it once did. However, removing pages did not change the identity of the book. It is still a book, even though it has fewer pages and therefore less volume and mass.

A physical change occurs every time you dissolve one substance in another substance. Perhaps you like iced tea. When you dissolve sugar in iced tea, the sugar seems to disappear. But if you heated the liquid so that it evaporates, you will see that the sugar is still there. Therefore, dissolving sugar in iced tea is an example of a physical change.

Recall that flammability is a chemical property of matter. After an object burns, new substances are produced. Burning is an example of a chemical change. A **chemical change** occurs when one or more substances are changed into new substances that have different properties. Chemical properties and chemical changes are not the same. A chemical change is the *process* by which a substance with certain chemical properties changes into a new substance with different chemical properties. For example, a chemical change takes place when wood is burned. New substances are produced that have different chemical properties. Wood is flammable. However, ashes are not flammable.

The following table lists other examples of physical and chemical changes.

Physical changes	Chemical changes
Chopping wood	Burning wood
Crushing an aluminum can	Dropping an aluminum can in acid
Slicing a tomato	Making tomato sauce
Boiling water	Adding an antacid tablet to water

Chemical Reactions

Another term for a chemical change is chemical reaction. A **chemical reaction** is a process in which one or more substances change to make one or more new substances. Recall that the properties of the new substances are different from those of the original substances.

Chemical reactions occur all around you. Examples of chemical reactions include leaves changing color in the fall, a cake baking in the oven, and gasoline burning in a car's engine. All these chemical reactions produce new substances. For example, the burning of gasoline produces carbon dioxide and water.

There are several signs that tell you that a chemical reaction may be occurring. In some chemical reactions, a color change occurs. This is what happens when leaves turn color in the fall. This is also what happens when bleach gets on clothing. If bleach spills on your blue jeans, a chemical reaction will take place and cause the color of the fabric to change.

In some chemical reactions, gas bubbles form. For example, if an electric current flows through water, gas bubbles are produced. The electric current causes a chemical reaction. In this reaction, water is changed into two new substances. These two substances are oxygen gas and hydrogen gas.

Other chemical reactions release energy. Energy can be released in the form of light, heat, or electricity. The burning of wood is a chemical reaction that releases both light and heat. The following table summarizes the signs that a chemical reaction has taken place.

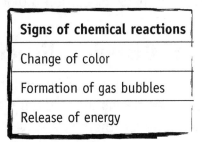

Signs of chemical reactions
Change of color
Formation of gas bubbles
Release of energy

Chemical Equations

Chemical reactions are described by using equations. Consider the chemical reaction that occurs when charcoal burns to cook food on a barbecue. This chemical reaction can be written as follows.

carbon + oxygen → carbon dioxide

The above equation is read as follows: Carbon reacts with oxygen to produce carbon dioxide. Carbon and oxygen are known as reactants. A **reactant** is a starting material in a chemical reaction. Notice that the reactants appear before the arrow in a chemical equation. Carbon dioxide is known as a product in this reaction. A **product** is a substance that is formed in a chemical reaction. Notice that the products appear after the arrow in a chemical equation.

Chemical reactions are usually written as chemical equations. A **chemical equation** uses chemical symbols and numbers to describe a chemical reaction. The reaction between carbon and oxygen is written as the following chemical equation.

$$C + O_2 \rightarrow CO_2$$

Notice that a chemical equation uses a form of shorthand known as a chemical formula. A **chemical formula** is a shorthand way to use chemical symbols and numbers to represent a substance. In the above equation, C is the chemical formula for carbon, O_2 is the chemical formula for oxygen, and CO_2 is the chemical formula for carbon dioxide.

Types of Chemical Reactions

There are many thousands of known chemical reactions. Remembering all of them would be impossible. However, there is a way to make it easier to study them. Chemical reactions can be classified or organized into groups based on what happens. Organizing chemical reactions into groups is similar to organizing books in a library. Imagine how difficult it would be to find a book if they were not organized according to some system.

One group of chemical reactions consists of synthesis reactions. A **synthesis reaction** is a reaction in which two or more reactants combine to form one product. The burning of charcoal to cook food is an example of a synthesis reaction.

$$C + O_2 \rightarrow CO_2$$

Notice that in the above reaction, the two reactants, C and O_2, combine to form one product, CO_2.

Another group of chemical reactions is known as decomposition reactions. A **decomposition reaction** is a reaction in which a single reactant breaks down to form two or more products. A decomposition reaction is the reverse of a synthesis reaction. The following chemical equation shows a decomposition reaction that occurs inside your body.

$$H_2CO_3 \rightarrow H_2O + CO_2$$

In this reaction, the reactant is a substance called carbonic acid. Carbonic acid, H_2CO_3, is transported in the blood. When carbonic acid reaches the lungs, it breaks down to form water, H_2O, and carbon dioxide, CO_2. The carbon dioxide is then exhaled from the lungs.

Lesson 1

Review

Darken the circle by the best answer.

1. Which are the reactants in the following chemical equation?

$$HCl + NaOH \rightarrow NaCl + H_2O$$

- Ⓐ HCl and NaCl
- Ⓑ NaOH and NaCl
- Ⓒ HCl and NaOH
- Ⓓ NaCl and H_2O

2. A physical change occurs
- Ⓐ whenever new substances are produced.
- Ⓑ when a piece of paper is torn in half.
- Ⓒ during a chemical reaction.
- Ⓓ if gas bubbles are produced when two substances are mixed.

3. Matter is defined as anything that has both
- Ⓐ mass and volume.
- Ⓑ mass and weight.
- Ⓒ color and mass.
- Ⓓ reactants and products.

4. Which of the following can be used to describe a chemical change?
- Ⓐ chemical symbol
- Ⓑ chemical formula
- Ⓒ chemical equation
- Ⓓ changes in physical properties

5. In a decomposition reaction,
- Ⓐ two substances are combined to form a single product.
- Ⓑ a physical change takes place.
- Ⓒ no new substances are produced.
- Ⓓ a single substance is broken down to form two or more products.

6. Which of the following indicates that a chemical change has occurred?
- Ⓐ mass decreases
- Ⓑ light is given off
- Ⓒ weight increases
- Ⓓ sugar dissolves

7. Why is the melting point of a substance considered a physical property, and not a chemical property?

_____

_____

8. How does a chemical equation show that a chemical change has taken place?

_____

_____

Lesson 1   Properties of Matter

Unscramble each of the following sets of letters to form a word from the list of *Key Terms* on page 7. Then use the circled letters to form the words that answer the question about matter.

1. s m a s   __ __ ◯ __

2. h e w i g t   __ __ __ __ __ ◯

3. t r u d p o c   ◯ ◯ __ __ __ __ __

4. c h i s a l y p   ◯ __ __ ◯ __ __ __ __

5. t r a t a n e c   ◯ __ __ __ ◯ __ __ __

6. c l i m a c h e   __ __ ◯ __ ◯ __ __ __

7. a n i t e q u o   ◯ __ __ __ __ ◯ ◯ __

What can change in matter?

__ __ __ __ __ __ __ __ __ __ __ __ __ __

Lesson 1   Changes in Matter

Determine whether each of the following statements is true or false by circling the appropriate letter. If the statement is false, rewrite it so that it is true.

1. A physical change produces new substances. T or F

_____

2. Another term for a chemical change is a chemical reaction. T or F

_____

3. The new substances made in a chemical reaction are called the products. T or F

_____

4. The boiling point of a substance is an example of a chemical property. T or F

_____

5. When wood burns, wood is considered a reactant. T or F

_____

6. Weight is a physical property of an object that does not change no matter where the object is located in the universe. T or F

_____

7. In a synthesis reaction, two or more substances are combined to form a single new substance. T or F

_____

8. A change in color is a sign of a chemical reaction. T or F

_____

9. In a chemical equation, the reactants are placed after the arrow. T or F

_____

Lesson 1

Physical and Chemical Changes

Use the following list of words to complete the passage about matter and changes of properties in matter. A word or words may be used more than once.

| chemical | chemical change | chemical equation | chemical reaction | mass |
| physical | physical change | products | reactants | volume |

Matter is considered anything that has both (1) _____ and

(2) _____ . The more matter an object has, the larger its

(3) _____ . The more space an object takes up, the larger its

(4) _____ . Matter has both (5) _____

and (6) _____ properties. A (7) _____

property can be observed or measured without changing the identity of the object. Any

change in a physical property is known as a (8) _____ . In

contrast, a (9) _____ is a change that produces a new substance.

Another term for this type of change is a (10) _____ .

A (11) _____ is written in a shorthand known as a

(12) _____ . In a (13) _____ , the

(14) _____ are shown on the left side of the arrow, and the

(15) _____ are shown on the right side of the arrow.

Lesson 1   Experiment: Changes in Water

You learned that a physical change does not involve a change in the identity of a substance. A chemical change involves the production of new substances. In this experiment, you will examine both physical and chemical changes in water.

You Will Need

thick, plastic bottle   small piece of cardboard
aluminum foil   scissors
freezer   two pencils
tall drinking glass   sharpener
tablespoon   two 12-inch pieces of bare copper wire
salt   9-volt battery

Procedure

1. Fill the bottle with water to the very top.

2. Tightly cover the opening with aluminum foil.

3. Place the bottle in a freezer overnight.

4. Check the bottle the next day.

5. Pour warm water into the glass so that it is about two-thirds full.

6. Add a tablespoon of salt and stir until it dissolves.

7. Cut the cardboard so that it completely covers the top of the glass.

8. Sharpen the pencils at both ends.

9. Carefully push the pencils through the cardboard about 1 inch apart from one another.

10. Wrap one end of each wire around a sharpened end of each pencil.

11. Connect the other ends of the wires to the battery.

Experiment: Changes in Water (cont'd.)

12. Place the cardboard on the glass so that the free ends of the pencils are in the water.

13. Watch what happens near the pencil points in the water.

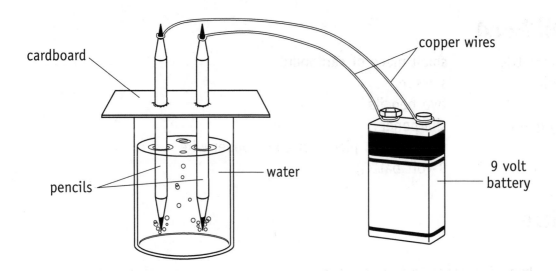

Results and Analysis

1. What kind of change did the water undergo in the freezer? _____

2. How does the volume of the ice (solid) compare to the volume of the water (liquid)?

_____

3. What kind of change did the water undergo in the glass? _____

4. What evidence indicated that a chemical reaction was occurring near the pencil points in the

water? _____

Conclusion

What conclusion can you draw from your observations?

_____

_____

Lesson 2 Motions and Forces

Have you ever pulled or pushed a sled through the snow? Or have you ever pulled or pushed a chair across the floor? By pulling and pushing, you made the sled or chair move. By pushing and pulling, you created a force. In turn, the force set an object in motion. In this lesson, you will learn about motions and forces.

Motions and Forces

Whenever you push or pull an object, you know if it's moving. But did you know that you can tell if an object is moving only by looking at another object at the same time? For example, you know that a chair is moving because it is sliding across the floor. You see that the chair moves while the floor stays in place. The object that stays in place is called a reference point. When an object changes position over time with respect to a reference point, the object is in **motion**.

An object cannot be set in motion until a force acts on it. A **force** is simply a push or a pull. Scientists express force using a unit called the **newton** (N). Usually, more than one force is acting on an object. However, no matter how many forces are acting on an object, the object may not move at all.

Suppose two teams are competing in a tug-of-war contest. Each team is pulling on the rope in the opposite direction. What happens if each team applies the same amount of force? Assume that a team applies

Key Terms

motion—the change in position of an object over time with respect to a reference point

force—a push or a pull

newton—the unit for force

net force—the combination of all the forces acting on an object

friction—the force that opposes motion between two surfaces that are in contact

fluid—a substance that can flow and take the shape of its container

pressure—the amount of force exerted on a given area

Bernoulli's principle—principle that states that as the speed of a moving fluid increases, its pressure decreases

atmospheric pressure—the pressure caused by the weight of the atmosphere

buoyancy—an upward force that fluids exert on all matter

Archimedes' principle—principle that states that buoyancy on an object in a fluid is an upward force that equals the weight of the fluid that the object displaces

a force of 100 N in one direction. Also assume that the other team applies a force of 100 N in the opposite direction. In this case, the forces cancel each other. The net force on the rope is zero. The **net force** is the combination of all the forces acting on an object.

100 N   100 N

Now assume that one team applies more force. For example, one team may start to pull with a force of 120 N. If the other team continues to apply a force of 100 N, then the net force is 20 N. The rope will move in the direction of the net force.

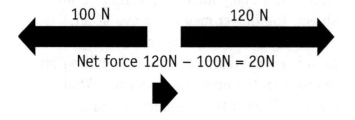
100 N   120 N
Net force 120N – 100N = 20N

Balanced and Unbalanced Forces

If the net force is zero, then the forces are said to be balanced. Balanced forces will not cause a nonmoving object to start moving. Balanced forces will also not cause any change in the motion of a moving object. If the net force is not zero, then the forces are said to be unbalanced. Unbalanced forces will cause a nonmoving object to start moving.

A kick is an unbalanced force that causes a soccer ball to move. Unbalanced forces will also change the motion of a moving object. Another kick can cause a moving soccer ball to change direction or move faster. An object can continue to move even after the force has been removed. The soccer ball will keep

moving after the force of the kick has been removed. However, at some point, the soccer ball will stop moving. Its motion stops because of another force.

Friction

The force that stops the ball is friction. **Friction** is the force that opposes motion between two surfaces that are in contact. Friction occurs because the surfaces of objects are rough. Some surfaces, like those of the pages in this book, feel smooth. However, if you look very closely at these surfaces with a microscope, you will see that they look jagged like the teeth on a saw. The tiny "teeth" on one surface can fit between the tiny "teeth" on the other surface. This causes friction.

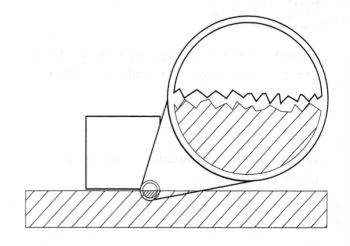

The rougher the surface is, the larger the "teeth" on the surface. Therefore, rougher surfaces cause more friction. This is why a soccer ball does not travel as far on the

Lesson 2, Motions and Forces
Science 6, SV 9781419034343

ground compared to a puck traveling across the ice. The ice has a very smooth surface. As a result, there is much less friction than there is on a soccer field. Because there is less friction, the puck can travel a greater distance than a soccer ball when the same amount of force is applied.

The amount of friction also increases when the forces pushing the surfaces together increase. Increasing the forces pushes the surfaces closer together. As a result, the "teeth" are in closer contact. Assume that you have two books that are the same size. However, one book has more pages and therefore more mass. There is more friction between the book with more mass and the table than there is between the book with less mass and the table. This is one reason why it takes more force to push the book with more mass across the table.

Friction can be useful. Friction between a basketball player's sneakers and the court allows the player to stop quickly to take a shot. Friction between a car's tires and the road prevents the car from slipping and sliding. However, friction can also cause problems. Friction between the moving parts of a car's engine can cause them to wear away. Oil is added to reduce friction.

Fluids and Motion

So far, your study of forces and motion has focused on solid objects, such as a rope and a soccer ball. However, forces and motions are also involved in liquids and gases. Gases and liquids are known as fluids. A **fluid** is any substance that can flow and take the shape of its container.

Because they flow, both air and water are fluids. You have probably heard of air pressure and water pressure. Both air pressure and water pressure are caused by particles that are constantly moving. For example, the air particles inside a car's tire are constantly moving and bumping into each other. These particles also collide against the walls of the tire. These collisions create a force against the walls. The amount of force is known as air pressure. **Pressure** is the amount of force exerted on a given area. The air pressure inside a tire may be 32 pounds per square inch, abbreviated as 32 psi. This means that the air particles are creating a pressure of 32 pounds on each square inch of tire.

Air Pressure and Motion

Differences in air pressure can create motion. A dramatic example is a tornado. The air pressure inside a tornado is very low. In contrast, the air pressure outside is very high. As a result, air moves very rapidly into a tornado where the pressure is lower. This rapidly moving air can lift and hurl huge objects, such as cars and trees.

Differences in air pressure are also responsible for the ability of an airplane to lift off and land. In the eighteenth century, a Swiss mathematician named Daniel Bernoulli discovered that as the speed of a moving fluid increases, its pressure decreases. This became known as **Bernoulli's principle.**

Airplane wings are made so that the air speed above the wing is different than the air speed below the wing. At takeoff, the air flow is faster above the wing than it is below the wing. Therefore, the air pressure is higher below the wing. This higher air pressure pushes up on the wing, lifting the plane. The higher air pressure creates enough force to overcome the force of gravity that is pulling down on the plane.

Atmospheric Pressure

The atmosphere consists of a layer of gases that surrounds Earth. These gases include oxygen, carbon dioxide, and nitrogen. Like all matter, these gases have mass and therefore weight. The weight of these gases is responsible for **atmospheric pressure**.

Atmospheric pressure is exerted on everything on Earth, including you. At sea level, it exerts a pressure of about 15 pounds on every square inch of your body, or about 10 N on every square centimeter. If there is this much atmospheric pressure on your body, then why don't you feel it? The answer is because of the pressure exerted by the fluids in your body. The fluids inside your body exert a pressure that equals the atmospheric pressure outside your body. Because the pressures are equal, they cancel each other's effect. As a result, you do not feel either pressure.

Water Pressure and Motion

Have you ever tried to push a cork under water? No matter how hard you try, the cork will always move back up to the surface. The water exerts a force on the cork. This force is called buoyancy. **Buoyancy** is an upward force that fluids, such as water, exert on all matter.

Over 2000 years ago, a Greek mathematician named Archimedes discovered how to determine buoyancy. **Archimedes' principle** states that buoyancy on an object in a fluid is an upward force that equals the weight of the fluid that the object displaces. To understand what this principle means, suppose a glass is filled to the top with water. Now suppose that you place a rock in the glass. Some of the water will overflow and spill from the glass. The weight of the water that overflows is the weight of the water that the rock displaces.

You learned in Lesson 1 that weight is a measure of the force of gravity on the mass of an object. To most people, the unit for weight is the pound (lb). However, to scientists, the unit of weight is the newton (N).

You know that a rock sinks in water. A rock sinks because its weight is greater than the weight of the water it displaces, which is the buoyant force on the rock. For example, assume that a rock weighs 50 N. Also assume that the weight of water the rock displaces, or buoyant force, is 30 N. The buoyant force of the water is not enough to support the rock. As a result, the rock sinks.

You also know that an iceberg floats in water. An iceberg floats because its weight equals the weight of the water it displaces, which is the buoyant force on the iceberg. For example, assume that an iceberg weighs 100,000,000 N. Also assume that the weight of the water the iceberg displaces is 100,000,000 N. The buoyant force of the water is enough to support the iceberg. As a result, the iceberg floats.

The following table summarizes why a rock sinks while an iceberg floats.

Object	Weight of object	Weight of water displaced (buoyant force)	Result
Rock	50 N	30 N	Sinks
Iceberg	100,000,000 N	100,000,000 N	Floats

Lesson 2

Darken the circle by the best answer.

1. If an object weighing 40 N displaces a volume of water that weighs 10 N, what is the buoyant force on this object?

   Ⓐ 50 N

   Ⓑ 40 N

   Ⓒ 30 N

   Ⓓ 10 N

2. The ability of an airplane to take off can be explained by

   Ⓐ Archimedes' principle.

   Ⓑ Bernoulli's principle.

   Ⓒ Newton's principle.

   Ⓓ buoyant forces.

3. Which of the following is a fluid?

   Ⓐ an ice cube

   Ⓑ a cork

   Ⓒ an airplane

   Ⓓ oxygen gas

4. An object is being pulled in one direction by a force of 10 N. The object is also being pulled in the opposite direction by a force of 15 N. The net force on this object is

   Ⓐ 5 N.

   Ⓑ 10 N.

   Ⓒ 15 N.

   Ⓓ 25 N.

5. A wet floor is slippery because the water

   Ⓐ increases friction.

   Ⓑ decreases friction.

   Ⓒ provides a buoyant force.

   Ⓓ is displaced by shoes walking on the floor.

6. What is needed to determine if an object is in motion?

   Ⓐ friction

   Ⓑ the object's mass

   Ⓒ a reference point

   Ⓓ balanced forces

7. Four separate forces are acting on an object, yet the object does not move. Explain how this is possible.

   _____

   _____

Lesson 2

Net Forces

You learned that the net force is the combination of all the forces acting on an object. If the forces are acting in the same direction, they must be added to get the net force on the object. If the forces are acting in opposite directions, then they must be subtracted to get the net force on the object. In each of the following problems, calculate the net force and tell in which direction the object will move.

1. A bicycle rider is applying a force of 20 N while heading south against a wind blowing from the south with a force of 5 N.

2. One boy is pushing a wagon down the driveway with a force of 6 N while another boy is pulling it up the driveway with a force of 4 N.

3. One girl is applying a force of 4 N to lift a box while another girl is applying a force of 3 N to lift the same box.

4. If the force of gravity on the box is 5 N, will the girls in the problem above be able to lift the box? Explain your answer.

5. Examine the following diagram. Calculate the net force and determine in which direction the object will move.

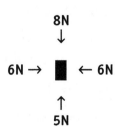

Lesson 2
Science Friction

Read the following passage and then answer the questions that follow.

Even though the weather was a bit chilly, Ben and his father decided to go on a camping trip for the weekend. Early Saturday morning, they drove to a local campsite. Ben's father had to drive slowly as it had rained heavily the night before. When they finally arrived, Ben and his father went hiking. They had just bought the same brand of hiking boots and were anxious to try them out. Ben had a little trouble keeping his footing as they climbed the rather steep trail.

When they returned to their campsite, they unpacked the car. After pitching their tent, they started a fire to cook dinner. But Ben's father had forgotten to pack matches. As a Boy Scout, Ben knew that a fire could be started by rubbing two sticks together.

While they were eating, Ben's father decided that it was a good opportunity to talk about a family matter. He mentioned that he had noticed there was a little friction lately between Ben and his older brother who was at college. Ben admitted that his older brother was concerned that Ben's grades were not as good as they should be. Ben promised that he would study harder.

1. Ben's father drove slowly to the campsite because

(A) it was difficult to see the road.

(B) he was not familiar with the route.

(C) he knew that the rain had reduced the friction between the car's tires and the road.

(D) he knew that the rain had increased the friction between the car's tires and the road.

2. Ben's father had no trouble climbing the steep trail because

(A) he had a better pair of hiking boots.

(B) his weight created more friction than Ben did with his boots.

(C) his boots had thicker soles.

(D) he knew the trail better than Ben.

3. Ben knew that friction could produce

(A) heat.

(B) a force.

(C) motion.

(D) pressure.

4. When is the word *friction* not used in a scientific sense?

(A) when describing the weather conditions

(B) when describing how Ben started a fire

(C) when describing how Ben's father drove

(D) when describing Ben's relationship with his brother

Lesson 2 — Motions and Forces Crossword Puzzle

Across

4. what the forces are said to be if the object does not move

8. person who explained why an object floats or sinks

9. what an object does in water if its weight is greater than the buoyant force

11. person who explained how a plane can take off

Down

1. substance that can flow

2. combination of all the forces acting on an object (2 words)

3. the kind of point you need to tell if an object is moving

4. upward force that keeps an object floating on a liquid, such as water

5. unit for force or weight

6. amount of force exerted on a given area

7. force that opposes motion

10. what friction can stop

Lesson 2   Pressure

You learned that the amount of force exerted on a given area is defined as the pressure. This definition can be written as an equation.

$$\text{pressure} = \frac{\text{force}}{\text{area}}$$

You learned that the unit for force is the newton (N). Scientists use meters squared (m^2) as the unit for area. The unit they use for pressure is called the pascal (Pa). 1 Pa = 1 N/m^2. Use the above equation to solve the following problems involving pressure.

1. Amanda pushes with a force of 10 N on a door to open it. If the area of her hand is 100 cm^2, what is the pressure exerted by Amanda's hand on the door? (Hint: The units will be N/cm^2.)

2. A rock weighs 2500 N and has an area of 10 m^2. What is the pressure that the rock exerts? Express your answer in pascals.

3. The water in a glass has a weight of 2.2 N. The bottom of the glass has an area of 0.022 m^2. What is the pressure exerted by the water on the bottom of the glass? Express your answer in pascals.

4. What is the weight of a book that exerts a pressure of 50 Pa and that has an area of 0.2 m^2? (Hint: You must rearrange the equation for pressure so that you solve for force, or weight in newtons.)

Lesson 2   Experiment: Reducing Friction

Friction can slow down and even stop a moving object. Therefore, reducing friction should allow an object to maintain its speed and even move faster than it normally does. A hovercraft is an example of how the movement of an object is affected by reducing friction. A hovercraft travels on a cushion of air above the water. Not coming in contact with the water reduces friction. As a result, the hovercraft can speed along the top of the water. In this experiment, you will build a model of a hovercraft.

What You Will Need

ruler	glue
pencil	wooden spool
cardboard	balloon
scissors	twist-tie
small nail	smooth flat surface

Procedure

1. Use the ruler to draw a square on the cardboard about 5 inches on each side.

2. Cut out the cardboard square.

3. Push a small nail through the center of the smoother side of the cardboard square. Then remove the nail.

4. Glue the wooden spool to the other side of the cardboard square. Make sure that the hole of the spool lines up with the hole in the cardboard. Allow the glue to dry thoroughly.

5. Blow up the balloon. Wrap the twist-tie around the neck of the balloon tightly so that air does not escape.

6. Place the neck of the balloon over the spool.

7. Hold your "hovercraft" over a smooth, flat surface.

8. Remove the twist-tie. Give your "hovercraft" a gentle push.

Experiment: Reducing Friction (cont'd.)

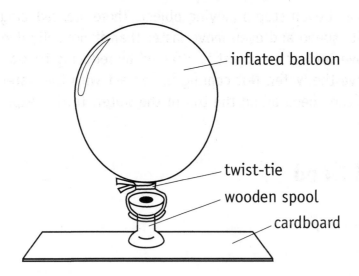

inflated balloon

twist-tie
wooden spool
cardboard

Results and Analysis

Describe what happened when you removed the twist-tie.

_____

_____

_____

_____

_____

_____

Conclusion

What conclusion can you draw based on your observations?

_____

_____

_____

_____

_____

Lesson 3 Transfer of Energy

There are days when you have more energy than other days. On the days that you have more energy, you can do more. You may take a long walk, ride your bicycle to a friend's house, or play a game of baseball. On days that you do not have that much energy, you may not do as much. You may watch TV, read a book, or talk on the telephone. In this lesson, you will learn more about energy and what it can do for you.

Energy

If you ask ten people what energy is, you are likely to get ten different answers. In science, however, energy has just one meaning.

Key Terms

energy—the ability to do work

work—the use of a force that causes an object to move in the direction of the force

potential energy—the energy an object has because of its position

kinetic energy—the energy an object has because of its motion

temperature—a measure of the average kinetic energy of the particles in an object

thermal energy—the kinetic energy of all the moving particles in an object

heat—the energy that is transferred between objects that are at different temperatures

conduction—the transfer of heat energy between two objects that are in direct contact

convection—the transfer of heat energy as the particles in a liquid or gas move

electromagnetic waves—waves that can travel through matter and empty space

radiation—the transfer of heat energy by electromagnetic waves

electrical energy—the energy of moving electrons

electron—a negatively charged particle that makes up part of an atom

atom—the basic building block of matter

electric current—the rate at which the electrons pass a given point in a wire

voltage—the amount of energy electrons release as they flow through a wire

series circuit—an electric circuit where all the parts are connected to form a single loop

parallel circuit—an electric circuit where all the parts are joined side by side

Energy is the ability to do work. **Work** is done when a force causes an object to move in the direction of that force. If the object does not move in the direction of the force, then no work is done and no energy is used.

Suppose you are on a team playing tug-of-war. Your team is pulling on the rope. However, the other team is pulling the rope in their direction. Because the rope is not moving in the direction of the force you are applying, then you are not doing any work. In a scientific sense, you are not using energy. With all that pulling, you may find this hard to believe!

Forms of Energy

A swimmer uses a lot of energy to win a race. The swimmer will depend upon two kinds of energy. When the swimmer is on the block and ready to jump into the pool, she has potential energy. **Potential energy** is the energy an object has because of its position. When she jumps into the pool and begins swimming, she has kinetic energy. **Kinetic energy** is the energy an object has because of its motion.

At the start of the race, potential energy is changed into kinetic energy as the swimmer begins to move through the water. At the end of the race, kinetic energy is changed into potential energy when the swimmer finishes and rests. The amount of potential energy at the end of the race, however, is less than the amount present at the start of the race. Much of the potential energy was changed into kinetic energy that was used to move the swimmer through the

water. Once the kinetic energy is used, it cannot be changed back into potential energy. To regain the potential energy she had at the start of the race, the swimmer must eat. Foods contain potential energy, which can be changed to kinetic energy.

Measuring Kinetic Energy

You have probably felt hot on a summer day when the temperature was over 90°F. On the other hand, you probably have felt cold on a winter day when the temperature was below 20°F. Temperature indicates how hot or cold something is. In science, **temperature** is defined as a measure of the average kinetic energy of the particles in an object.

You learned in Lesson 1 that all matter is made of particles that are always moving. The faster the particles move, the more kinetic energy they have. The more kinetic energy the particles of an object have, the higher the temperature of the object is.

Not all particles in an object are moving at the same speed. Some are moving faster than others. As a result, the particles have different amounts of kinetic energy. However, there is an average kinetic energy for all these particles, just as there is an average grade for all the grades on a test. When you measure an object's temperature, you are measuring the average kinetic energy of its particles.

Temperature does not depend on how much there is of an object. For example, suppose you boil water in a kettle. You then pour some of the water into a cup to make tea. Although there is more hot water in the kettle, the temperature of the water in the cup is the same as the temperature of the water in the kettle.

Thermal Energy

The kinetic energy of all the moving particles in an object is known as its **thermal energy**. Notice that thermal energy depends on the kinetic energies of *all* the particles in an object. In contrast, temperature is a measure of the *average* kinetic energy of all the particles in an object. Therefore, an object with a lower temperature may have a higher thermal energy than an object with a higher temperature. For example, a lake has a lower temperature than a cup of boiling water. But the lake, which has much more water, has a higher thermal energy than the cup of boiling water.

Heat

So far you looked at the words *hot* and *cold* in terms of kinetic energy, temperature, and thermal energy. But what about heat? Scientists define **heat** as the energy that is transferred between objects that are at different temperatures. Heat energy will always be transferred from the object with the higher temperature to the object with the lower temperature. This transfer of heat energy continues until both objects have the same temperature. Remember that the objects may have different thermal energies even though they have the same temperature.

Heat energy is sometimes transferred between two objects that are in direct contact. This transfer of energy is known as **conduction**. For example, conduction occurs when you touch an ice cube. Heat energy is quickly transferred from your hand to the ice cube.

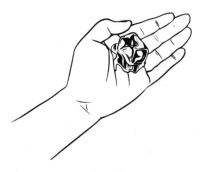

Heat energy can also be transferred as the particles in a liquid or gas move. This transfer of energy is known as **convection**. As the gases in the air get warmer, they rise. As they rise, they cool and then begin to sink back toward the ground. This process continues, setting up a pattern of air circulation. You may have seen an example of convection when you noticed the air flowing above the surface of a hot object, such as a radiator.

Heat energy can also be transferred as waves that can travel through both matter and empty space. These waves are known as **electromagnetic waves**. The transfer of heat by electromagnetic waves is called **radiation**. A portable heater transfers heat energy by radiation. When a person absorbs the electromagnetic waves, he or she feels warmer.

Electrical Energy

A portable heater radiates heat energy with the help of another type of energy. This is electrical energy. **Electrical energy** is the energy of moving electrons. An **electron** is a negatively charged particle that makes up part of an atom. An **atom** is the basic building block of matter.

When you use electrical energy, the electrons usually flow through a wire. The rate at which the electrons pass a given point in the wire is called the **electric current**. There are two kind of electric current. One kind is called *direct current*, abbreviated as DC. In direct current, the electrons always flow in the same direction. The electric current from the batteries used in a flashlight is DC.

The other kind of current is called *alternating current*, or AC. In AC current, the electrons continually shift from flowing in one direction to flowing in the reverse direction. The outlets in your home provide AC current. A portable electric heater is powered by AC current.

Voltage

As electrons flow through a wire, they release energy. The amount of energy they release is called **voltage**. The more energy the electrons release, the higher the voltage. The voltage determines the size of the electric current flowing through a wire. A greater current means that more electrons move in a wire each second. A large current is needed to start a car. Therefore, a car battery has a fairly high voltage. A car battery is an example of a 12-volt battery. Not as much voltage is needed to turn on a flashlight. A flashlight battery is an example of a 1.5-volt battery.

Electric Circuits

To generate electrical energy, electrons must travel in a circuit. A circuit is a pathway that ends where it starts. An electric circuit consists of three parts. One part is a power source, such as a battery, which provides the electrons. The second part consists of the wires through which the electrons travel. The third part is called a load. A load may be a radio, computer, or a portable heater. A load changes electrical energy into another form of energy. For example, a radio changes electrical energy into sound energy.

There are two ways to construct an electric circuit. One circuit is known as a series circuit.

In a **series circuit**, all the parts are connected to form a single loop. In a series circuit, the electrons follow the same path.

Series Circuit

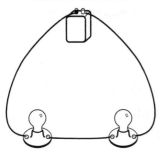

If there is any break in a series circuit, the electrons will stop flowing. A series circuit would not be a good way to wire all the electrical outlets in a house. If a break occurred in any room, none of the devices in the house would work. However, a series circuit works well for a burglar alarm system. If there is a break anywhere in the system, an alarm will sound.

Another type of electric circuit is a parallel circuit. In a **parallel circuit**, all the parts are joined side by side. In a parallel circuit, the electrons can flow through more than one path.

Parallel Circuit

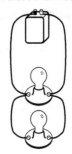

If there is a break in a parallel circuit, the electrons will keep flowing. If one load is broken or missing, the other loads can still operate. A parallel circuit is used in homes so that if one light is missing or broken, the others will still work. However, a parallel circuit would not be suitable for an alarm system because it may not sound the alarm if there is a break in any part of the system.

Lesson 3

Review

Darken the circle by the best answer.

1. You can feel the warmth of the sun in summer. How is heat transferred from the sun to Earth?

Ⓐ conduction

Ⓑ convection

Ⓒ radiation

Ⓓ current

2. The random motion of all the particles in an object represents its

Ⓐ thermal energy.

Ⓑ heat.

Ⓒ potential energy.

Ⓓ electrical energy.

3. Which of the following statements about a parallel circuit is true?

Ⓐ A parallel circuit does not contain any loads.

Ⓑ Electrons flow in only a single path.

Ⓒ The failure of one load does not affect another load.

Ⓓ No electrons flow through the circuit.

4. Heat is always transferred

Ⓐ between objects with different thermal energies.

Ⓑ when kinetic energy is changed into potential energy.

Ⓒ as electrons.

Ⓓ from an object with a higher temperature to an object with a lower temperature.

5. The amount of energy released by electrons as they travel through a circuit is known as the

Ⓐ current.

Ⓑ voltage.

Ⓒ alternating current.

Ⓓ direct current.

6. Temperature is a measure of

Ⓐ potential energy.

Ⓑ thermal energy.

Ⓒ average kinetic energy.

Ⓓ electrical energy.

7. Describe how the transfer of heat differs between conduction and convection.

_____

_____

_____

_____

Lesson 3

Calculating Work

You learned that work involves the use of force to move an object in the direction of that force. You also learned that kinetic energy is the energy an object has because of its motion. You can calculate the amount of work that is done if you know the force and distance. The following equation is used to calculate the amount of work done.

$$\text{work} = \text{force} \times \text{distance} \text{ or } W = F \times d$$

In Lesson 2, you learned that the unit for force is the newton (N). The unit for distance is the meter (m). Therefore, the unit for work is the newton-meter, which is also called the joule (J). Use the above equation to solve the following problems involving work.

1. Suppose you and a friend both apply a force of 50 N to push a box of books 10 m across the floor. How much work did you do together?

2. Suppose you and a friend work together to apply a force of 75 N to lift a box of books 3 m off the floor. How much work did you do together?

3. Suppose you apply a force of 60 N to pull a tree branch 5 m. Your friend applies a force of 50 N to pull the same branch another 6 m. Who did more work?

4. Suppose you and your friend decide to push a bookcase to the other side of a room. Together, you apply a force of 1200 N. The bookcase weighs 100 kg. The distance across the room is 5 m. However, no matter how hard you push, the bookcase does not move. How much work did you and your friend do?

Lesson 3
Energy, Temperature, and Heat

Write the letter of the word or words on the right in front of the appropriate definition or description on the left. A letter can be used more than once.

_____ **1.** transfer of thermal energy through space

_____ **2.** measure of average kinetic energy

_____ **3.** energy due to motion

_____ **4.** transfer of thermal energy through contact

_____ **5.** transferred thermal energy

_____ **6.** transfer of thermal energy through a gas

_____ **7.** energy due to position

_____ **8.** type of waves that travel through space

_____ **9.** transfer of thermal energy through a liquid

_____ **10.** kinetic energy of all the particles in an object

a. thermal energy

b. convection

c. electromagnetic

d. potential energy

e. temperature

f. radiation

g. conduction

h. heat

i. kinetic energy

Lesson 3, Energy, Temperature, and Heat
Science 6, SV 9781419034343

Lesson 3

Electric Circuits

You learned that all the parts form a single loop in a series circuit. In contrast, a parallel circuit includes parts that are joined in branches. A switch can be placed at any point in a branch. The switch must be closed to complete the circuit. If a switch is open, then electrons cannot flow past that point. Use the following diagram of a parallel circuit to answer the questions that follow.

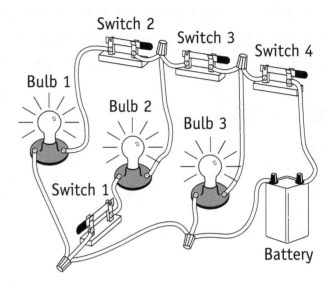

1. What will happen if Switch 1 is open?

_____

2. What will happen if Switch 3 is open?

_____

3. Is it possible for only Bulb 1 to be lit? Explain your answer.

_____

_____

4. Is it possible for Bulb 2 to be lit while Bulb 3 is off? Explain your answer.

_____

_____

5. Is it possible to open just one switch to turn off all three bulbs? Explain your answer.

_____

_____

Lesson 3   Experiment: Using the Heat from the Sun

You learned that electromagnetic waves travel to Earth from the sun. Once they reach Earth, these waves can produce a feeling of warmth. In this experiment, you will trap the heat from the sun to cook a hot dog.

You Will Need

empty shoe box
aluminum foil
nail
pliers
unpainted wire clothes hanger
liquid soap
hot dog

CAUTION: Adult supervision required.

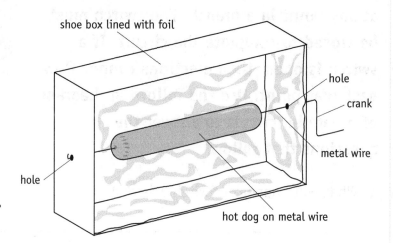

Procedure

1. Line the inside of the shoe box with aluminum foil.

2. Use the nail to poke a tiny hole in each end of the shoe box slightly below the middle.

3. Use the pliers to straighten the hanger. Bend one end of the hanger to make a crank. You may need the help of an adult to shape the hanger.

4. Wash the hanger with soap and water.

5. Insert the straight end of the wire hanger through one end of the shoe box.

6. Carefully push the hot dog on to the wire hanger.

7. Insert the end of the wire hanger through the hole at the other end of the shoe box. Bend the end of the wire slightly.

8. Place the shoe box in bright sunlight. Do not look directly at the sunlight reflected off the foil.

9. Occasionally turn the handle so that the hot dog cooks evenly. Discard the hot dog.

Experiment: Using the Heat from the Sun (cont'd.)

Results and Analysis

1. Describe what happens to the hot dog.

_____

2. How is heat transferred from the sun to your shoe box?

_____

3. How is heat transferred from your shoe box to the hot dog?

_____

Conclusion

What conclusion can you draw based on the results of your experiment?

_____

_____

_____

_____

_____

_____

_____

_____

_____

_____

_____

Lesson 4 Structure and Function in Living Systems

What happens when you take a closer look at something? Most likely, you see things that you did not see before. Perhaps you notice a stain on your favorite pants. Or maybe you discover a crack in a window when you try to open it. Scientists also discover things when they take a closer look with the help of special instruments. For example, they use microscopes to take a closer look at living things. As a result, scientists have discovered much about the structure and function in living systems.

Cells

All living things are made of tiny structures called cells. A **cell** is the smallest unit that can carry out all the processes necessary for life. For example, a cell carries out digestion and respiration. Cells come in all shapes and

Key Terms

cell—the smallest unit that can carry out all processes necessary for life

organism—a living thing

unicellular—an organism that is made of a single cell

multicellular—an organism that is made of more than one cell

organelle—a part that makes up a cell

cell membrane—organelle that covers a cell's surface and controls what enters and leaves a cell

nucleus—organelle that directs much of the cell's processes

mitochondrion—organelle that produces energy

endoplasmic reticulum—organelle where many chemical reactions occur

ribosome—organelle where proteins are made

Golgi complex—organelle that packages proteins

lysosome—organelle that digests food materials and destroys harmful particles

cell wall—a rigid structure that supports a plant cell

chloroplast—organelle where a plant cell makes food

photosynthesis—the process plants use to make food

tissue—a group of cells that work together to perform a specific job

organ—a group of two or more tissues that work together to perform a specific job

organ system—a group of organs that work together to perform a specific job

sizes. Some cells are round while others are long and thin. Most cells are too small to see without a microscope. For example, it would take 50 human skin cells to cover the dot on this letter *i*. However, some cells are quite large. A cell that is over six feet long stretches the length of a giraffe's neck.

Microscopes allowed scientists to take a closer look at **organisms**, or living things. What they saw led them to develop the cell theory. This theory has three parts.

The Cell Theory
1. All organisms are made of one or more cells.
2. The cell is the basic unit of all living things.
3. All cells come only from other cells.

Notice that the first part of the cell theory states that an organism can be made of just one cell. Such organisms are said to be **unicellular**. The most common unicellular organisms are bacteria. Bacteria are the smallest cells known. The first part of the cell theory also states that an organism can be made of many cells. Such organisms are said to be **multicellular**. A human is an organism that is made of billions of cells.

Cell Structure

All cells contain certain basic parts. These cell parts are called **organelles**. Each organelle carries out a specific function. One organelle that all cells have is the cell membrane. The **cell membrane** is a protective barrier that encloses a cell. It separates the cell's contents from the cell's environment and controls what enters and leaves a cell. For example, digested food materials pass through the cell membrane and enter the cell where they are used for energy.

Another organelle is the nucleus. The **nucleus** contains the cell's genetic material. Because it directs several processes that occur within the cell, the nucleus is sometimes referred to as the "control center."

Cells produce energy in an organelle called the mitochondrion. A **mitochondrion** processes the energy in food substances such

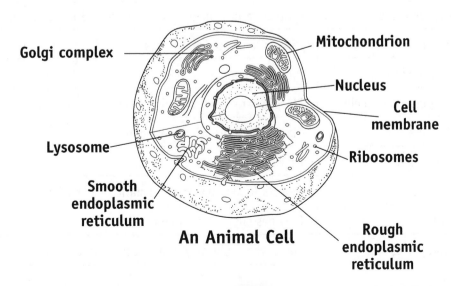

Golgi complex

Mitochondrion

Nucleus

Cell membrane

Lysosome

Ribosomes

Smooth endoplasmic reticulum

Rough endoplasmic reticulum

An Animal Cell

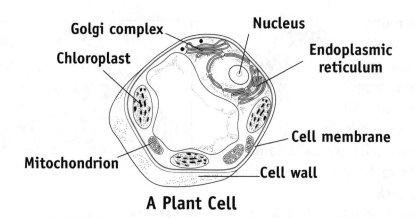

A Plant Cell

as sugars. The energy from these substances is then stored in a chemical called ATP. The cell then uses ATP to do work.

Many chemical reactions take place in a cell. Many of these reactions occur on or in an organelle called the endoplasmic reticulum. The **endoplasmic reticulum**, abbreviated ER, is a system of folded membranes that extend through much of the cell. Part of the ER is covered with ribosomes. A ribosome is the smallest organelle. A **ribosome** is the place where proteins are made in the cell. In a cell, there are more ribosomes than any other organelle.

Another organelle is the Golgi complex, named after an Italian scientist who first discovered it. The **Golgi complex** packages the proteins made on the ribosomes. The Golgi complex looks like ER that is not covered with ribosomes. The proteins that are packaged by the Golgi complex can then pass to other parts of the cell. These proteins may also pass through the cell membrane and travel to other parts of the organism.

Digestion occurs inside a cell in an organelle called a **lysosome**. These organelles come in a wide variety of sizes and shapes. In addition to digestion, lysosomes also destroy harmful particles that might enter the cell. If they were not destroyed, these particles might damage or even kill the cell.

Plant cells contain two structures that are not found in animal cells. One of these is the cell wall. A **cell wall** is a rigid structure that

The following table lists some of the organelles and their main functions.

Organelle	Function
Cell membrane	Protects and controls what enters and leaves a cell
Nucleus	Directs many cell processes
Mitochondrion	Produces energy
Endoplasmic reticulum	Place where many chemical reactions occur
Ribosome	Place where proteins are made
Golgi complex	Packages proteins
Lysosome	Digests foods and destroys harmful particles
Cell wall	Provides support for plant cell
Chloroplast	Place where photosynthesis occurs in plants

gives support to the cell. The cell wall surrounds the cell membrane. Plant cells also contain chloroplasts. A **chloroplast** is the place where photosynthesis occurs. **Photosynthesis** is the process by which plants use sunlight, carbon dioxide, and water to make sugar and oxygen.

Cells Work Together

You learned that a multicellular organism is made of more than one cell. Multicellular organisms, such as humans, contain billions of cells. All these cells must work together. If they did not work together, then the organism would not function properly. Just imagine what would happen if all the workers in a car assembly plant did not work together. You would never get a car that works.

Cells that work together to perform a specific job make up a **tissue**. For example, the cells in a muscle work together as a unit that is called muscle tissue. Nerve cells in the muscle work together as a unit called nerve tissue.

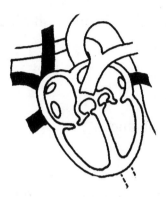

Notice that both muscle tissue and nerve tissue work together in a muscle. A structure that is made up of two or more tissues working together is called an **organ**. For example, the heart is an organ. The heart is made mostly of cardiac tissue, but it also contains nerve tissue.

The heart is part of the circulatory system. An **organ system** consists of organs that work together to perform a specific function. The human body contains several organ systems, including the digestive, respiratory, and nervous systems. Together, all the organ systems make up an organism. The following illustrations show the different levels of organization in living systems in two different ways.

cell → tissue → organ →
organ system → organism

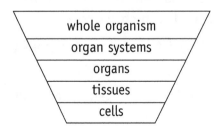

Lesson 4

Review

Darken the circle for the best answer.

1. Which organelle is found in both animal and plant cells?
   - (A) chloroplast
   - (B) cell wall
   - (C) cell membrane
   - (D) proteins

2. What function does a lysosome perform?
   - (A) digests food materials and destroys harmful particles
   - (B) produces proteins
   - (C) packages proteins
   - (D) controls what enters and leaves the cell

3. Which of the following statements is part of the cell theory?
   - (A) All organisms are composed of one or more cells.
   - (B) Most cells are too small to be seen without a microscope.
   - (C) Cells exist in different shapes and sizes.
   - (D) Bacteria are unicellular organisms.

4. Which of the following shows the correct order of levels of organization?
   - (A) cell→organ→tissue→organ system→organism
   - (B) organ→tissue→cell→organ system→organism
   - (C) cell→organism→organ→tissue→organ system
   - (D) cell→tissue→organ→organ system→organism

5. Muscle cells have a high energy requirement. Which organelle is most likely to be found in large numbers in a muscle cell?
   - (A) chloroplast
   - (B) lysosome
   - (C) mitochondrion
   - (D) Golgi complex

6. Where does photosynthesis occur in a plant cell?
   - (A) nucleus
   - (B) chloroplast
   - (C) endoplasmic reticulum
   - (D) ribosome

7. How is it possible that some organisms do not have organ systems?

_____

_____

_____

Lesson 4   Cell Structures and Functions

Write the correct letter of the term from Column B that is described in Column A. A letter may be used more than once.

Column A

_____ **1.** uses sunlight to make food

_____ **2.** uses food to make ATP

_____ **3.** where chemical reactions occur

_____ **4.** where harmful particles are destroyed

_____ **5.** protects an animal cell

_____ **6.** supports a plant cell

_____ **7.** makes proteins

_____ **8.** packages proteins

_____ **9.** stores genetic information

_____ **10.** directs many cell processes

_____ **11.** where photosynthesis occurs

_____ **12.** where digestion occurs

_____ **13.** named after an Italian scientist

_____ **14.** name for a single-celled organism

_____ **15.** what wastes must pass through

_____ **16.** what is found on ER (not the television show)

Column B

a. nucleus

b. lysosome

c. Golgi complex

d. chloroplast

e. unicellular

f. mitochondrion

g. endoplasmic reticulum

h. cell membrane

i. cell wall

j. ribosome

Lesson 4   The Black Reaction

Read the following passage and then answer the questions.

Camillo Golgi was born in Italy in 1843. After graduating from medical school, Golgi worked in a hospital. He converted a small kitchen into a laboratory where he began his studies of the nervous system. Golgi created a new method to stain individual nerve cells. Staining cells makes them easier to study under a microscope.

However, nerve cells are not as easy to stain as other cells. Nerve cells have long thin branches that do not stain easily. Golgi developed a new staining method that used a chemical compound called silver nitrate. This compound stains nerve cells black. Therefore, Golgi's method of staining nerve cells became known as the black reaction. The black reaction enabled scientists to study individual nerve cells. Golgi's method is still used today to stain nerve cells.

In 1885, Golgi published drawings that he had made of the brain and spinal cord. The black reaction allowed Golgi to see and draw these structures in detail. Before Golgi's work, scientists were not sure that the cell theory applied to the nervous system because no one had been able to observe these cells in detail. Golgi's work showed that the nervous system supported the cell theory. Golgi was awarded a Nobel Prize in 1906 for his contributions to our knowledge of cells.

1. The black reaction is a process that Golgi used to
   A dissolve nerve cells.
   B remove the parts of nerve cells.
   C make nerve cells more visible under a microscope.
   D remove nerve cells from the brain.

2. Golgi studied to become a(n)
   A illustrator.
   B chemist.
   C writer.
   D doctor.

3. Which of the following statements is true?
   A Scientists still use Golgi's staining procedure.
   B Golgi showed that the cell theory did not apply to the nervous system.
   C Golgi did not share his discoveries with others.
   D Nerve cells are easy to see under a microscope.

4. What is the main idea of this passage?
   A Golgi won a Nobel Prize in 1906.
   B Golgi converted a kitchen into a laboratory.
   C Golgi's work provided valuable information about the nervous system.
   D Golgi was a doctor who did research.

Lesson 4 Experiment: Taking Out the Green

You learned that photosynthesis occurs in chloroplasts. Photosynthesis uses sunlight to make food and oxygen. Chloroplasts collect sunlight with the help of a chemical substance called chlorophyll. Chlorophyll is a colored substance called a pigment. In this experiment, you will take out the chlorophyll from a green plant and then check to see if other pigments are also present. Be sure to do this experiment with adult supervision because you will use a stove and a flammable substance.

You Will Need

spinach leaves
scissors
small pot
rubbing alcohol
stove
coffee filter
ruler
toothpick
tape
pencil
drinking glass

CAUTION: Adult supervision required. Use a vent hood when heating the alcohol.

Procedure

1. Cut up some spinach leaves and place them in a small pot.

2. Cover the leaves with rubbing alcohol.

3. Heat gently. Be very careful as alcohol is flammable.

4. Continue heating until the alcohol turns a dark green color.

5. Turn off the stove and allow the alcohol to cool.

6. Cut the coffee filter into a 1-inch by 6-inch strip.

7. Use a toothpick to place a drop of the green alcohol close to the bottom of the filter paper along the 1-inch edge. Allow the drop to dry.

Experiment: Taking Out the Green (cont'd.)

8. Repeat step 7 until you have a dark green spot on the filter paper.

9. Tape the other end of the filter paper to the middle of the pencil.

10. Set the pencil on top of the glass so that the filter paper hangs inside the glass.

11. The bottom edge of the filter paper should be about $\frac{1}{2}$ inch from the bottom of the glass. If the filter paper is too long, remove it from the pencil, and cut it so that it hangs properly. If the paper is too short, use a shorter glass.

12. Remove the pencil and paper from the glass. Carefully pour rubbing alcohol into the glass. Pour enough alcohol so that when you hang the filter paper in the glass, the alcohol will touch the bottom edge. However, the dark green spot must be above the level of the alcohol.

13. Allow the paper to remain in the alcohol. Remove the paper when the alcohol has almost moved up to the top of the paper.

14. Remove the filter paper and allow it to dry on a paper towel.

Results and Analysis

1. Describe the appearance of the filter paper. _____

_____

2. What happened as the alcohol moved up the coffee filter?

_____

_____

Conclusion

What conclusion can you draw based upon your results?

_____

_____

Lesson 5   Reproduction and Heredity

Do you remember the last time you scraped your arm or leg? A scab may have formed on your skin where you injured yourself. Slowly, the scab disappeared as new skin cells replaced those that had been damaged. Your body is constantly making new cells to replace those that are damaged or die. In addition to skin cells, your body continuously makes new blood cells. In fact, your body makes millions of new cells every second. In this lesson, you will learn how cells produce new cells.

Heredity

A human passes through different stages of life, beginning with birth. Cells also pass through different stages. These stages make up the **cell cycle**. The cell cycle begins when a cell is formed. The next stage involves growth. Growth is followed by a stage where the cell prepares to form new cells. The cell cycle ends when the cell divides and forms new cells.

Before a cell divides, a copy must be made of the hereditary material it contains. **Heredity** is the passing of traits from one generation to the next. For example, you might have curly hair just like your mother. Or you may have brown eyes just like your father.

Key Terms

cell cycle—the life cycle of a cell

heredity—the passing of traits from parents to offspring

DNA—the chemical substance that controls the structure and function of cells

chromosome—the cell structure that stores the hereditary information

homologous chromosomes—a pair of chromosomes with the same structure that contain hereditary information for the same traits

mitosis—the process of cell division that forms two nuclei that contain identical DNA

daughter cell—a cell produced by the division of a parent cell

sperm—the male sex cell

egg—the female sex cell

fertilization—the joining of an egg and sperm

meiosis—the process of cell division that forms sex cells, each of which has half the number of chromosomes as found in the parent cell

cytokinesis—the division of the cytoplasm of a cell

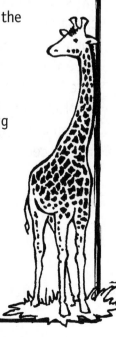

These are traits that you inherited from your parents. In some cases, traits that neither parent has may appear in the offspring. For example, both parents who have brown eyes may have a child with blue eyes. Heredity can be more complicated than it appears.

The hereditary information that determines an individual's traits is contained in a chemical substance called deoxyribonucleic acid, or DNA. **DNA** is the hereditary material that controls the structure and function of cells. As a result, DNA determines an individual's traits. The DNA inside a cell is organized into structures called **chromosomes**. Some unicellular organisms, such as bacteria, have a single, circular chromosome. The chromosomes of multicellular organisms, such as humans, are more complex.

Humans have 46 chromosomes. The number of chromosomes is not an indication of how complex an organism is. For example, potatoes have 48 chromosomes. However, the information stored in the 48 potato chromosomes is not nearly as complex as the information stored in the 46 human chromosomes.

The 46 human chromosomes come in pairs. Therefore, there are 23 pairs of human chromosomes. Each pair is known as a homologous pair. **Homologous chromosomes** have the same shape and contain the hereditary information for the same traits. The following illustration shows the 23 homologous pairs of chromosomes in a human cell.

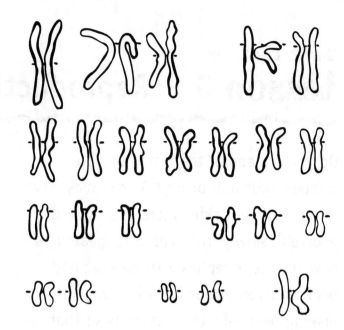

Mitosis

Assume that you make a copy of each page in this book. As a result, you would have two books, each with a complete set of information. You can give one copy to each of two friends. Each person would then have all the information that was contained in the original book.

A similar process occurs in a cell. During the growth stage of the cell cycle, called the interphase, a copy is made of each chromosome. At this point, the cell has two complete sets of the hereditary information. The next stage of the cell cycle is known as mitosis. **Mitosis** is a division that forms two nuclei. Each nucleus will have the same number and kind of chromosomes that were present in the parent cell. As a result of mitosis, each cell receives a complete set of the hereditary information.

Remember that a copy of each chromosome is made before mitosis begins. The copy is attached to the original. Each is known as a *chromatid*. Mitosis begins when the chromosomes shorten. They appear as rod-like structures under a microscope.

Lesson 5, Reproduction and Heredity
Science 6, SV 9781419034343

The following diagram shows only four chromosomes (eight chromatids) so that it is easier to follow what happens during mitosis.

In the next step, the chromosomes line up along the equator of the cell. Notice that the chromatids are still attached to each other.

In the next step, the chromatids separate and move toward opposite sides of the cell.

In the final step of mitosis, the cell membrane begins to pinch in, as shown in the next illustration.

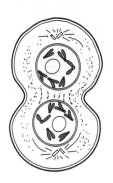

Eventually the cell membrane pinches all the way through the cell. This produces two cells. Each cell has the same number and kind of chromosomes that were present in the parent cell. The two new cells are called **daughter cells**. The daughter cells are identical to each other and to their parent cell.

Meiosis

Most of the cells in the human body reproduce by mitosis. For example, mitosis produces new skin cells to replace those that are damaged from a scrape or cut. However, certain cells in the body cannot be produced by mitosis. These are the sex cells. Sex cells include sperm and egg cells that are involved in reproduction.

The sex cells produced by the male are called **sperm**. The sex cells produced by the female are called **eggs**. A sperm cell and an egg cell unite or join to form a single cell. The joining of the sperm and egg is called **fertilization**.

Human sex cells contain only 23 chromosomes, or half the number found in most cells. Each sex cell has only one of the chromosomes from each homologous pair. When a sperm cell fertilizes an egg, the 23 chromosomes from each sex cell will be combined. Therefore, the fertilized egg will contain 46 chromosomes.

The process that makes sex cells is called meiosis. **Meiosis** produces sex cells that contain half the original number of chromosomes. Recall that in mitosis, the chromosomes are copied once. In meiosis, the chromosomes are also copied once. The following illustrates what happens when human chromosomes are copied.

The Cell Cycle

46 chromosomes in a body cell.
↓
46 chromosomes are copied in preparation for nuclear division.
↓
92 chromosomes. Half (46) go to each new nucleus before the cell divides.

Recall that in mitosis, the nucleus divides once. However, in meiosis, the nucleus divides twice. Each nuclear division is followed by a cell division known as cytokinesis. During **cytokinesis**, the cytoplasm divides into approximately equal halves. As a result, each of the four sex cells have half the number of chromosomes.

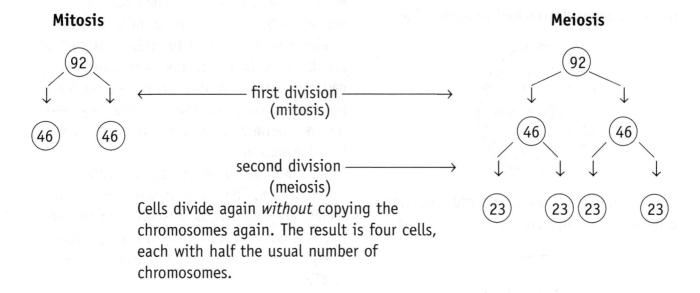

Mitosis

Meiosis

first division (mitosis)

second division (meiosis)

Cells divide again *without* copying the chromosomes again. The result is four cells, each with half the usual number of chromosomes.

Puberty

Meiosis produces mature sex cells. The sex cells are said to be mature because they can participate in fertilization. Each mature human sex cell has 23 chromosomes. An immature sex cell has 46 chromosomes. An immature sex cell must undergo meiosis to become mature. Only then can the sex cell participate in fertilization. Sex cells begin to mature when a person reaches puberty. During puberty, a person's reproductive system becomes mature.

In most boys, puberty takes place between the ages of 11 and 16. During this time, a young male's body becomes more muscular, his voice deepens, and body and facial hair appear. At this point in his life, a young male can start producing mature sperm. In most girls, puberty takes place between the ages of 9 and 14. During this time, a young female's body develops more fat in the thighs and hips, the breasts enlarge, and the menstrual cycle begins. At this point in her life, a young female can start producing mature eggs.

Lesson 5   Review

Darken the circle for the best answer.

1. After mitosis is complete, how many daughter cells are produced following cytokinesis?

Ⓐ one

Ⓑ two

Ⓒ three

Ⓓ four

2. If an immature sex cell contains 18 chromosomes, how many chromosomes are present in a mature sex cell?

Ⓐ 9

Ⓑ 18

Ⓒ 36

Ⓓ 46

3. How are mitosis and meiosis similar?

Ⓐ Both produce mature sex cells.

Ⓑ Both produce four daughter cells.

Ⓒ Both involve a division of the nucleus.

Ⓓ Both reduce the chromosome number by half.

4. Which of the following statements is true?

Ⓐ Meiosis produces cells with identical DNA.

Ⓑ Mitosis stops when a human reaches adulthood.

Ⓒ Meiosis is necessary before fertilization can occur.

Ⓓ Mitosis does not pass on any hereditary information to the daughter cells.

5. What process can be completed only when puberty starts?

Ⓐ cell growth

Ⓑ copying of chromosomes

Ⓒ mitosis

Ⓓ meiosis

6. Which human cell does *not* contain 46 chromosomes?

Ⓐ brain cell

Ⓑ mature egg cell

Ⓒ fertilized egg cell

Ⓓ immature egg cell

7. What would happen if mature sex cells were produced by mitosis instead of meiosis?

_____

_____

_____

Lesson 5

The Cell Cycle

The following graph shows the cell cycle. Use this graph to answer the questions.

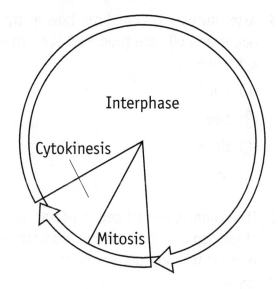

1. What is the correct order in which the
   parts of the cell cycle occur?

   _____

   _____

2. Which two parts of the cell cycle last about the
   same amount of time?

   _____

   _____

3. Which part of the cell cycle is the longest?

   _____

4. Why is the cell cycle represented by a pie graph or circle?

   _____

   _____

5. Describe what happens during the part of the cell cycle that is called mitosis.

   _____

   _____

6. Describe what happens during the part of the cell cycle that is called cytokinesis.

   _____

   _____

Lesson 5   **Mitosis**

The following diagram illustrates a cell that is undergoing mitosis. Use this illustration to answer the questions.

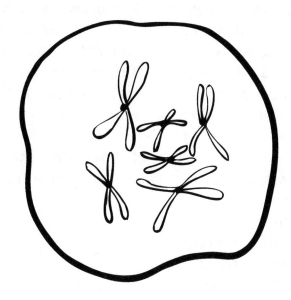

1. How many chromosomes does this cell contain?

_____

2. How many homologous pairs of chromosomes does this cell contain?

_____

3. How many chromatids does this cell contain?

_____

4. How many chromosomes will be present in each daughter cell after the cell shown above divides?

_____

5. Explain why the daughter cells will have the identical hereditary information as the parent cell.

_____

_____

Lesson 5   The Sex Chromosomes

Read the following passage and then answer the questions.

The 46 chromosomes in a human cell exist as homologous pairs. In females, the members of each pair have a similar structure. However, in males, there is a pair of homologous chromosomes which do not have a similar structure. One is shorter than the other. This pair is known as the sex chromosomes. Sex chromosomes determine the sex of an individual.

The role of the sex chromosomes was discovered in 1905 by a scientist named Nettie Stevens. She became one of the first female scientists to make a major discovery. At that time, no one knew how the sex of an individual was determined. Stevens used a microscope to examine the chromosomes in various insects. She noticed that half of the sperm cells in insects contained a chromosome not found in eggs. She concluded that this tiny structure inside the sperm determines sex.

Stevens proposed that, except in sperm and eggs, chromosomes exist in pairs. She also proposed that the small chromosome seen in some sperm cells was a member of a homologous pair. The other member of this pair was a chromosome that had recently been seen in female cells, including eggs. Today, scientists know that human females have two sex chromosomes known as X chromosomes. But human males have one X chromosome and one Y chromosome. Stevens had discovered this smaller Y chromosome.

Meiosis produces eggs that all have an X chromosome. However, meiosis produces sperm with either an X or Y chromosome. An egg fertilized by a sperm with an X chromosome will produce a female. If the sperm contains a Y chromosome, the offspring will be male.

1. How do the chromosomes of a human female differ from those of a human male?

_____

_____

_____

2. Why was Nettie Stevens's discovery important?

_____

_____

_____

3. Explain why the sex of an individual is determined by the sperm and not the egg.

_____

_____

_____

Lesson 5   Experiment: Growth and Mitosis

Cells have both volume and surface area. The volume is the amount of space that is inside the cell. The surface area is the total area of the cell membrane that is exposed to the outside. As a cell grows, its volume and surface area do not increase at the same rate. In this experiment, you will make a model of two cells and see what might happen to a cell if it gets too large. Ask an adult to help you because you will be using a sharp knife and a stove.

You Will Need

knife	bowl	small drinking glass
red cabbage	unflavored gelatin	tablespoon
measuring cup	deep tray or baking pan	liquid ammonia
small pot	ruler	paper towel
stove	refrigerator	water
cheesecloth or coffee filter		

CAUTION: Adult supervision required. Make sure space is well ventilated.

Procedure

1. Chop the cabbage into small pieces.

2. Add 2 cups of the chopped cabbage to a small pot. Cover with water and boil for 10 minutes.

3. Allow the liquid to cool to room temperature.

4. Pour the contents of the pot through the cheesecloth or coffee filter. Collect the purplish liquid in a clean container.

5. Prepare the gelatin according to the directions on the package. Add some of the purplish liquid to the gelatin.

6. Pour the colored gelatin into the tray. The gelatin in the tray must be at least 1 inch deep.

7. Place the gelatin in the refrigerator until it solidifies.

Experiment: Growth and Mitosis (cont'd.)

8. Cut the gelatin into two cubes. One cube should measure $\frac{1}{2}$ inch on each side. The other cube should measure 1 inch on each side.

9. Carefully place both cubes in the glass.

10. Cover the cubes with water. Add 1 tablespoon of ammonia.

11. Allow the cubes to soak for 10 minutes.

12. Carefully pour the liquid down the sink drain. Rinse the cubes with water several times.

13. Place the cubes on a paper towel.

14. Cut both cubes in half.

Results and Analysis

1. Ammonia causes the red pigment in cabbage to turn green. Ammonia seeps into both cubes. Describe the appearance of each cube.

_____

_____

2. A smaller cube has a higher ratio of surface area to volume than a larger cube. How does this higher surface area to volume ratio affect how ammonia seeps into the cube?

_____

_____

Conclusion

What conclusion can you draw based on your results?

_____

_____

Lesson 6 Regulation and Behavior

All organisms must be able to obtain and use resources. These resources include nutrients and oxygen. All organisms must also be able to get rid of waste products, such as carbon dioxide. As a result, organisms are constantly exchanging materials with their environment. This exchange occurs between each cell of an organism and its environment. As a result of these exchanges, cells maintain stable internal conditions while living in a constantly changing environment. In this lesson, you will learn how cells exchange materials with their environment.

Diffusion

Any materials that a cell exchanges with its environment must pass through the cell membrane. Diffusion is one process by which materials pass through a cell membrane. **Diffusion** is the movement of particles from areas of higher concentration to areas of lower concentration. Diffusion occurs whenever someone pours milk into their coffee. At first, the concentration of milk is higher where it is first poured into the coffee. The milk then slowly spreads out, or diffuses, throughout the coffee. Stirring the coffee speeds up the process so that the milk diffuses through the coffee faster.

Diffusion is the process by which cells get oxygen. In humans, oxygen is taken in

Key Terms

diffusion—the movement of particles from areas of higher concentration to areas of lower concentration

alveolus—a tiny air sac in the lung

capillary—a tiny blood vessel

osmosis—the diffusion of water through a semipermeable membrane

state of equilibrium—a condition where the concentrations of a substance remain equal

homeostasis—the maintenance of a stable internal environment

contractile vacuole—an organelle that maintains water balance in unicellular organisms

passive transport—the movement of particles without the use of energy

active transport—the movement of particles with the use of energy

endocytosis—the process by which a cell membrane surrounds a particle and then brings it inside the cell

exocytosis—the process by which a cell releases a large particle

through the nose and eventually reaches the lungs. Each lung is made up of tiny air sacs called **alveoli**. Each lung contains about 300 million alveoli. Each alveolus is surrounded by a tiny blood vessel called a **capillary**. Both an alveolus and a capillary are surrounded by a wall made of only a single cell layer. As a result, materials can easily pass across the cell membranes.

In the lungs, the concentration of oxygen is higher in the alveoli than it is in the capillaries. Therefore, oxygen diffuses from the alveoli into the capillaries. The blood in the capillaries then transports the oxygen to all the cells in the body. In contrast, the concentration of carbon dioxide is higher in the capillaries than it is in the alveoli. Therefore, carbon dioxide diffuses from the capillaries into the alveoli. The carbon dioxide eventually passes into the nose or mouth where it is exhaled into the environment.

When the blood reaches a cell in the body, the concentration of oxygen is higher in the blood than it is in the cell. Therefore, oxygen diffuses from the blood into the cell. In contrast, the concentration of carbon dioxide is higher in the cell than it is in the blood. Therefore, carbon dioxide diffuses from the cell into the blood. The blood eventually returns to the lungs to continue the diffusion of oxygen and carbon dioxide.

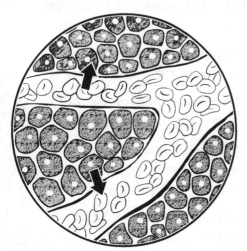

Osmosis

The cells of an organism are surrounded by fluids that are made mostly of water. Water moves through cell membranes by a process called osmosis. **Osmosis** is the diffusion of water through a *semipermeable* membrane. Semipermeable means that only certain substances can pass through the cell membrane.

Examine the following illustration which shows how diffusion and osmosis occur across cell membranes.

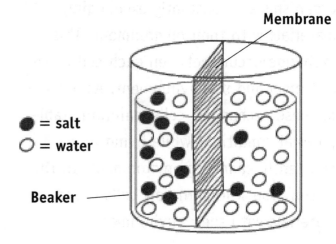

= salt
= water

The membrane shown in the above illustration allows both salt and water to pass through it. Notice that the concentration of salt is higher on the left side, while the concentration of water is higher on the right side. Salt will diffuse from left to right. Water will move by osmosis from right to left. Both salt and water will diffuse until the concentrations of both substances are equal on both sides of the membrane. When the concentrations are equal, a **state of equilibrium** has been reached.

Although the concentrations are equal in a state of equilibrium, substances continue to diffuse. For example, a salt particle may diffuse from the left side to the right side. When this happens, a salt particle on the right side will diffuse to the left side. As a result, there is no change in the concentrations of salt on either side.

Osmosis in Plant Cells

Have you ever seen a wilted plant? The reason the plant is wilted can be explained by osmosis. A plant wilts because there is little or no water outside the root cells. Therefore, water is in a higher concentration inside these plant cells. As a result, water moves out of the cells into the surrounding soil. As the cells lose water, they shrink and the plant wilts.

When a wilted plant is watered, the water concentration is higher outside the root cells. Water moves by osmosis into the cells. As a result, osmosis makes the plant firm again.

Homeostasis

Osmosis is important to cell functions. For example, red blood cells are surrounded by a fluid called plasma. Plasma is mostly water. Plasma also contains salts, sugars, and other dissolved substances. The concentrations of water, salts, sugars, and other substances must be kept in balance. Cells must maintain a stable internal environment to survive. The maintenance of a stable internal environment is called **homeostasis.**

Even single-celled organisms must exhibit homeostasis. Consider paramecium, a unicellular organism that lives in freshwater streams and ponds.

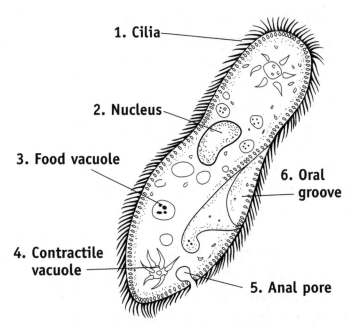

1. Cilia
2. Nucleus
3. Food vacuole
4. Contractile vacuole
5. Anal pore
6. Oral groove

The water concentration inside a paramecium must be kept in balance with the water concentration in the external environment. Consider what would happen if the water concentration outside the paramecium became higher than it is inside. Water would move by osmosis through the cell membrane and into the paramecium. The organism would begin to fill with water and swell up. If too much water moves in, the organism may burst and die.

To prevent this from happening, a paramecium contains an organelle called a **contractile vacuole.** Locate the contractile vacuole in the above illustration. This structure fills with water and then pumps it out of the paramecium. As a result, the contractile vacuole eliminates the water that moves in by osmosis. By eliminating the excess water, the contractile vacuole plays a role in homeostasis.

Transport

Diffusion and osmosis occur without the use of energy. Because they do not require energy, diffusion and osmosis are examples of passive transport. **Passive transport** always involves the movement of particles from an area of high concentration to an area of lower concentration until a state of equilibrium is reached.

There are conditions, however, where passive transport will not meet the needs of a cell. Under these conditions, particles may move across a cell membrane by a process called active transport. **Active transport** is the movement of particles that requires energy. Active transport moves particles from an area of low concentration to an area of high concentration. Particles can move across a cell membrane by active transport only if energy is supplied. Active transport moves small particles across the membrane. These small particles include sugars that a cell needs for energy. As a result of active transport, a cell can get more sugar than it would by diffusion.

Large particles can also move across a cell membrane with the use of energy. One process that cells use to take in large particles is called endocytosis. **Endocytosis** is the process by which a cell membrane surrounds a particle and then brings it inside the cell. In humans, specialized white blood cells use endocytosis to take in bacteria and other tiny organisms that can cause disease.

Once inside the white blood cell, the bacteria are destroyed by the lysosomes. The following illustrations show the active-transport process of endocytosis.

 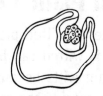 

Another active-transport process cells use is exocytosis. **Exocytosis** is the process by which a cell releases a large particle. You learned that the Golgi complex is the organelle that packages materials, such as proteins, for release by the cell. The materials are packaged in tiny structures called vesicles. The vesicle travels to the cell membrane and fuses with it. The cell then releases the particle to the outside of the cell. The following illustrations show the active-transport process of exocytosis.

Lesson 6   Review

Darken the circle for the best answer.

1. Which process requires energy?

   (A) diffusion

   (B) osmosis

   (C) endocytosis

   (D) passive transport

2. Which process results in a state of equilibrium?

   (A) diffusion

   (B) endocytosis

   (C) exocytosis

   (D) active transport

3. Which of the following is involved in the movement of particles into and out of a cell?

   (A) nucleus

   (B) lysosome

   (C) Golgi complex

   (D) cell membrane

4. The process in which particles move from an area of low concentration to an area of high concentration is called

   (A) diffusion.

   (B) osmosis.

   (C) passive transport.

   (D) active transport.

5. Which substance diffuses from an alveolus into a capillary?

   (A) carbon dioxide

   (B) oxygen

   (C) sugar

   (D) water

6. Which substance diffuses from a capillary into an alveolus?

   (A) carbon dioxide

   (B) oxygen

   (C) sugar

   (D) water

7. Homeostasis is defined as the

   (A) movement of materials from an area of high concentration to an area of low concentration.

   (B) use of energy to move materials through a cell membrane.

   (C) maintenance of a stable internal environment despite changes in the external environment.

   (D) ability to get rid of excess water from a cell.

8. Why does active transport require energy?

   _____

   _____

Lesson 6   The Big Eaters

Read the following passage and then answer the questions.

There is only one type of red blood cell circulating in your body. However, there are several types of white blood cells. One type of white blood cell is called a macrophage. The word *macrophage* comes from two Greek words that mean "big eaters." Macrophages play an important role in defending the body against disease. They carry out their role by destroying or "eating" bacteria and other invaders that can cause disease.

When a disease-causing invader enters the body, macrophages respond by surrounding it. The macrophage then takes in the invader by endocytosis. The invader winds up enclosed in a vesicle inside the macrophage. The next step is for a lysosome to fuse with the vesicle. Proteins in the lysosome can then mix with the contents of the vesicle. These proteins destroy the invader in the vesicle.

Unfortunately, macrophages do not always have an easy job of destroying invaders. In fact, in some cases, the invader can be difficult to destroy. An example is tuberculosis, a disease caused by bacteria. The bacteria that cause tuberculosis can be "eaten" by macrophages. However, these bacteria have a way to prevent a lysosome from fusing with the vesicle. As a result, the proteins in the lysosome cannot be released into the vesicle to destroy the invader. Other macrophages must be called in to complete the job.

Bacteria have other ways to protect themselves against the "big eaters." The bacteria that cause anthrax are surrounded by a protective coating. This coating makes it difficult for a macrophage to "eat" the bacterial invader by endocytosis.

1. Explain why macrophages are known as "big eaters."

_____

_____

2. How do the bacteria that cause tuberculosis avoid being destroyed by the "big eaters?"

_____

_____

3. How do the bacteria that cause anthrax avoid being destroyed by the "big eaters?"

_____

_____

4. How would a decreased number of macrophages affect a person's health?

_____

_____

Lesson 6   Diffusion and Osmosis

The following illustration shows a beaker that has been divided in half by a semipermeable membrane. This membrane will allow both water and food coloring particles to pass through it.

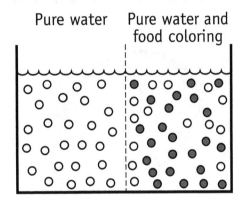

1. In which side is the concentration of water higher? In which direction will water move?

_____

_____

_____

2. In which side is the concentration of food coloring higher? In which direction will the food coloring move?

_____

_____

_____

3. Redraw the beaker to show the final concentrations of water and food coloring on both sides of the semipermeable membrane.

Lesson 6   Experiment: Diffusion and Osmosis

You learned that diffusion is the movement of materials from an area of high concentration to an area of low concentration. You also learned that osmosis is the diffusion of water through a semipermeable membrane. In the following experiment, you will see how diffusion and osmosis affect a potato, which is made of cells filled with starch.

You Will Need

adult helper
three large cups
masking tape
marker
tablespoon
salt
sugar
potato
knife
water

Procedure

1. Fill each cup about half full of water and place them on a flat surface.

2. Use the tape and marker to label one cup "water," another cup "salt," and the third cup "sugar."

3. Add two tablespoons of salt to the cup labeled "salt." Stir until all the salt dissolves. Keep adding salt and stirring until no more salt dissolves. Rinse the spoon.

Experiment: Diffusion and Osmosis (cont'd.)

4. Add two tablespoons of sugar to the cup labeled "sugar." Stir until all the sugar dissolves. Keep adding sugar and stirring until no more sugar dissolves.

5. Ask the adult to cut three slices from the middle of the potato. Each slice should be about $\frac{1}{4}$ to $\frac{1}{2}$ inch thick. Place one slice in each cup. Allow the potato slices to soak for at least 30 minutes.

6. Take the potato slice out of each cup and examine it.

Results and Analysis

Describe each potato slice. How are they different from each other?

_____

_____

_____

_____

Conclusion

What conclusions can you draw based on your results?

_____

_____

_____

_____

_____

_____

_____

_____

_____

_____

Lesson 7 Populations and Ecosystems

Every organism interacts with other living things. In some cases, the relationship between two living things benefits both. In other cases, the relationship benefits one living thing while not affecting the other in any way. Still other relationships benefit one living thing at the expense of the other. In this lesson, you will look at these various types of relationships.

Populations and Ecosystems

Organisms that share characteristics are often members of the same species. A **species** is a group of organisms that can mate with one another to produce fertile offspring. For example, all humans are members of the same species. The members of a species that live in a particular area make up a **population**. The population of your town or city consists of all the people who live there.

Populations along with the nonliving factors in their environment make up an

Key Terms

species—a group of organisms that can mate with one another to produce fertile offspring

population—the members of a species that live in a particular area

ecosystem—a group of populations and their nonliving environment

symbiosis—the relationship between two different organisms that live in close association with each other

mutualism—a symbiotic relationship in which both organisms benefit

commensalism—a symbiotic relationship in which one organism benefits and the other organism is not affected in any way

parasitism—a symbiotic relationship in which one organism benefits and the other organism is harmed

parasite—the organism that benefits in a parasitic relationship

host—the organism that is harmed in a parasitic relationship

predator—an organism that eats all or part of another organism

prey—an organism that is killed and eaten by another organism

adaptation—a feature that increases an organism's chance to survive and reproduce

competition—the interaction between two organisms trying to use the same natural resources

niche—the role an organism plays in its environment

ecosystem. For example, an ecosystem would include all the populations of species that live in your town or city plus all the nonliving factors found there. These nonliving factors include the air, soil, and water. Ecosystems are places where organisms are constantly interacting with one another and their nonliving environment.

Symbiosis

The relationship between two different organisms that interact closely is known as **symbiosis**, or a symbiotic relationship. Symbiotic relationships exist between plants and animals, bacteria and animals, fungi and plants, and so on. The thousands of symbiotic relationships in nature are often classified into three groups: mutualism, commensalism, and parasitism.

Mutualism

A symbiotic relationship in which both organisms benefit is known as **mutualism**. Mutualism can be seen in many flowering plants. These plants are visited at certain times of the year by insects. The insects benefit by getting nectar or nutrients from the plant. In turn, the plant benefits by having its pollen carried off by the insect. The pollen can be deposited some distance away on another plant. Here the pollen begins the process of producing another plant. Therefore, the insect serves as a pollinator and benefits the plant by helping it to reproduce.

An example of mutualism can be seen in the iris plant. Honeybees, which live on nectar, obtain it from plants such as the iris. In turn, honeybees are well suited to serve as pollinators for the iris. Honeybees have tongues that are almost 2.5 centimeters (1 inch) long, making it easier to pick up the sticky pollen inside the flower. Pollen also sticks to the honeybee's hairy body.

Mutualism also plays an important role in coral reefs. Coral reefs form in shallow, tropical seas. The reefs are built up over a long period of time by tiny organisms called polyps. These polyps live in a mutualistic relationship with algae. The polyps provide shelter for the algae. In turn, the algae provide food for the polyps' photosynthesis. Because of this mutualism between polyps and algae, a coral reef can grow to be quite large. The Great Barrier Reef off the coast of Australia is the largest coral reef in the world. It would stretch along the entire Eastern coast of the United States, reaching from Maine down to Florida.

Commensalism

A symbiotic relationship where one organism benefits and the other organism is not affected in any way is called **commensalism**. An example of commensalism can be seen in the mockingbird. Mockingbirds build their nests low to the ground in shrubs and trees. They use dead twigs and leaves to build a nest, filling it with grass and discarded items such as paper and plastics. Each mating pair produces two to three broods per season, with the female laying a total of about nine eggs. Mockingbirds benefit from the protection the trees and shrubs provide their nests. In contrast, the trees and shrubs are neither benefited nor harmed by the presence of the nests.

Another example of commensalism is seen in the relationship between sharks and a smaller fish called a remora. The remora attaches itself to the underside of a shark. The remora gets a "free ride" as the shark swims through the water. The remoras benefit by feeding off scraps of food left by the sharks. While the remora benefits in this relationship, the shark is unaffected.

Parasitism

A symbiotic relationship where one organism benefits at the expense of another organism is called **parasitism**. The organism that benefits is known as a **parasite**. The organism that is harmed is called the **host**. Most parasites do not kill their hosts. If the parasite were to kill its host, the parasite would have to find a new host.

An example of parasitism can be seen in the raccoon. Raccoons are hosts to numerous parasites, including one that can cause disease in humans.

One parasite is commonly known as the raccoon roundworm because it lives in the digestive tract of raccoons. The parasite may burrow into the raccoon's intestines where it can cause minor but not serious damage. The raccoon roundworm is actually more of a threat to humans. The microscopic eggs of the parasite are shed in raccoon feces. Young children and toddlers are more likely than adults to ingest the eggs by putting dirt and other objects into their mouth. After the eggs hatch, the roundworms can travel to the brain and muscles, where they can cause paralysis and even death.

Fortunately, the risk of infection is rare and remote. Nevertheless, the following precautions are recommended:

- Avoid direct contact with raccoons, especially their feces. Do not keep, feed, or adopt a raccoon as a pet. Remember that raccoons are *wild* animals.
- Discourage raccoons from living in and around your home or parks by removing access to food.
- Stay away from areas and materials that might be contaminated by raccoon feces.

Predators and Prey

Many interactions between species involve one organism eating another organism. The organism that eats another organism is called a **predator**. The organism that is eaten is called the **prey**. When a coyote eats a prairie dog, the coyote is the predator and the prairie dog is the prey.

Predators must be able to catch their prey. Predators have a variety of adaptations to do so. An **adaptation** is a feature that increases an organism's chances to survive and reproduce. For example, one adaptation that a coyote has is the ability to run very quickly to catch its prey. The coyote's speed gives it an advantage over other organisms that are also trying to catch a prairie dog.

Other predators hide and wait until their prey is within striking distance. These predators have adaptations that help them blend in with their environment. This type of adaptation is known as *camouflage*. The goldenrod spider depends on camouflage to hide from its insect prey. A goldenrod spider blends in so well with the goldenrod flower that it is difficult to spot. Insects that land upon a goldenrod flower will likely become a meal for the goldenrod spider that hides there.

Prey also depend upon camouflage. An insect commonly known as a walking stick is a perfect example. A walking stick looks like a twig. A predator, such as a bird, that sees a walking stick on a tree cannot recognize it. As a result, the walking stick does not become a meal for a bird.

In some cases, camouflage may not be so apparent. An example is the zebra. With its black and white stripes, a zebra would seem to be an easy target for a lion. However, lions are colorblind. To a lion, a zebra standing in tall grass looks just like its environment. While you can easily spot the zebra, the lion cannot distinguish it from the tall blades of grass.

Competition

Resources in the environment are often in limited supply. As a result, organisms must often compete for these resources, such as food and water. When two or more organisms try to obtain the same resources, it is called **competition**. Competition occurs among the members of a population. For example, the elks in Yellowstone National Park compete for the same plants. In winter, this competition can become intense because few plants are available.

Competition also occurs between different populations. For example, the trees and shrubs in a forest compete with one another for sunlight and water that they need for photosynthesis. Taller plants can capture the sunlight, while plants with an extensive root system can absorb the water.

In nature, competition is often avoided because organisms have different niches. A **niche** is the role an organism plays in its environment. A niche is not only the place where an organism lives but also what it eats, how it behaves, and how it interacts with other organisms.

Warblers are an example of organisms that survive by having different niches. Warblers are migratory birds. They spend the winter in the tropics and fly to northern forests in early spring to set up territories, mate, and rear their young. There are five species of warblers that spend their summers in a spruce forest in northern Maine.

These warblers are similar in body size and beak size, and they all feed on insects. However, all five species survive by living in different parts of a spruce tree and feeding on the insects they find there. If the birds from two different species do find themselves in the same part of the tree, one searches for food in the bark, while the other probes among the needles. All five species of warblers survive not by competing with one another but by having a different niche.

Lesson 7

Review

Darken the circle by the best answer.

1. Which term includes the other three?

   Ⓐ mutualism

   Ⓑ commensalism

   Ⓒ parasitism

   Ⓓ symbiosis

2. Bacteria are usually associated with disease. However, a certain type of bacteria lives in the digestive tract of cattle. The cattle provide a place for the bacteria to live, while the bacteria help to digest plant material. What type of relationship exists between these bacteria and the cattle?

   Ⓐ mutualism

   Ⓑ commensalism

   Ⓒ parasitism

   Ⓓ predator—prey

3. In the southeastern United States, it is common to see egrets in cattle pastures. They follow the cattle, eating insects that fly away as the cattle graze in the field. Removing the insects provides no obvious benefit to the cattle. What type of relationship exists between the egrets and the cattle?

   Ⓐ mutualism

   Ⓑ commensalism

   Ⓒ parasitism

   Ⓓ predator—prey

4. Five different kinds of lice are known to feed upon cattle in the United States. Lice bring about itching and skin irritations, causing the cattle to scratch, rub, and bite infested areas. What type of relationship exists between the lice and the cattle?

   Ⓐ mutualism

   Ⓑ commensalism

   Ⓒ parasitism

   Ⓓ predator—prey

5. What conclusion can be drawn from the information presented in questions 2, 3, and 4?

   Ⓐ All bacteria are parasites.

   Ⓑ One organism can provide examples of mutualism, commensalism, and parasitism.

   Ⓒ Both egrets and lice are beneficial to cattle.

   Ⓓ Relationships between two different organisms must always benefit both organisms.

6. What do predators and prey possess to increase their chances of survival?

   Ⓐ adaptations

   Ⓑ the same food source

   Ⓒ the same niche

   Ⓓ parasites

7. To avoid competition, two organisms must

Ⓐ share the same space.

Ⓑ seek the same prey.

Ⓒ not depend on their environment.

Ⓓ have different niches.

8. Explain why a parasite rarely kills its host.

_____

_____

_____

_____

9. Describe an example of two organisms that exhibit commensalism.

_____

_____

_____

_____

Lesson 7

Ecosystem Crossword Puzzle

Across

3. organism that is harmed in a symbiotic relationship

5. all the members of a species that inhabit a particular area

10. feature that increases an organism's chances of survival

11. role an organism plays in its environment

12. relationship in which one organism benefits and the other organism is not affected

13. a group of populations and their nonliving environment

Down

1. blending in with the background

2. relationship in which both organisms benefit

4. interaction between two organisms trying to use the same resources

6. group of organisms that can mate with one another and produce fertile offspring

7. organism that eats all or part of another organism

8. relationship between two different organisms in close association

9. organism that benefits at the expense of another organism

Lesson 7

The Termite—Is It a Pest or a Benefit?

Read the following passage and then answer the questions that follow the passage.

Most people consider termites to be pests. These insects can cause a lot of damage. One especially destructive pest is the Formosan termite. This species is twice the size of other termites and eats six times as much. Termites eat wood, chewing away at the foundation that supports a house. However, Formosan termites also chew through sheetrock, foam insulation, and even electrical cables to get to the wood they crave. They will even squeeze through a tiny crack to climb up to the wooden beams that support the roof of a house.

Wood is made mostly of a substance called cellulose. Termites cannot actually digest cellulose to obtain the energy that it contains. Rather, they chew and grind up the cellulose into smaller pieces. Bacteria and other tiny organisms that live in the termite's digestive tract then digest the cellulose into sugars. The termites can then use these sugars as an energy source. In turn, the termites provide a safe place for the tiny organisms to live.

Termites are adapted to live in a variety of places. Desert termites are able to survive the intense heat of the desert by building mounds. Some of their mounds can be nearly forty feet high, or as tall as a four-story building. These tall mounds help drive the circulation of air to keep the termites cool. Desert termites feed upon dead plant material and the solid wastes of animals. Without

termites, this material would decompose very slowly. Scientists estimate that without the help of termites, animal feces would cover about one-quarter of the Sonoran Desert in Arizona in just fifty years.

1. What type of relationship exists between the termites and the tiny organisms that live inside them? Explain your answer.

_____

_____

_____

_____

_____

_____

2. Is the termite a pest or a benefit? Explain your answer.

_____

_____

_____

_____

_____

_____

www.harcourtschoolsupply.com
© Harcourt Achieve Inc. All rights reserved.

75

Lesson 7, The Termite—Is It a Pest or a Benefit?
Science 6, SV 9781419034343

Lesson 7

A Striking Resemblance

Read the following passage and then answer the questions that follow the passage.

Scarlet kingsnakes are among the most beautiful of all snakes. Their vibrant colors and small size make them the jewels of the local ecosystem. These harmless snakes rarely get more than two feet long. They feed on a variety of small animals including lizards, small snakes, and newborn mice. Scarlet kingsnakes are rarely seen because they are very secretive. They spend their days under bark and fallen leaves, moving over land at night.

Coral snakes look much like scarlet kingsnakes. They too have beautiful colors, consisting of alternating rings of black, bright yellow, and deep red. Averaging only 20 inches or so, this snake is seldom seen and tends to be active only at night. The snake spends much of its life underground in cracks and crevices. The diet of the coral snake consists primarily of small lizards, snakes, reptiles, and amphibians.

Although these two snakes look much alike, they are actually quite different. The scarlet kingsnake is harmless. In contrast, the coral snake belongs to the same family as cobras. Like a cobra, the coral snake produces a powerful poison. If it bites a person, the poison can quickly paralyze the diaphragm, the muscle that controls breathing.

The bright colors of the coral snake serve as a warning to possible predators, such as foxes, coyotes, and raccoons. Upon seeing the colored bands on a coral snake, these predators are likely to move on to search for another prey rather than risk being bitten. These predators are likely to behave the same way when they see a scarlet kingsnake with

its similar bands of color. These snakes are an example of mimicry. A **mimic** is a harmless species that bears a striking resemblance to a harmful species and is therefore avoided by predators. Mimicry can be a lifesaver.

1. Both scarlet kingsnakes and coral snakes
   - (A) are poisonous.
   - (B) are harmless.
   - (C) can inhabit the same areas.
   - (D) use camouflage as a survival mechanism.

2. Which statement is true?
   - (A) Both scarlet kingsnakes and coral snakes are carnivores.
   - (B) Scarlet kingsnakes and coral snakes display mutualism.
   - (C) Competition is common between scarlet kingsnakes and coral snakes.
   - (D) Both scarlet kingsnakes and coral snakes are members of the same species.

3. Which is an adaptation for a scarlet kingsnake?
   - (A) production of a venom that can paralyze its prey
   - (B) camouflage
   - (C) speed
   - (D) being a mimic of a poisonous species of snakes

Lesson 7   Experiment: Competition Among Plants

All organisms require certain resources for growth and reproduction. Organisms that live in a resource-poor habitat, or are living with more organisms than the habitat can sustain, are not likely to do as well as those in better habitats with more resources. Organisms of the same species are most likely to compete for essential resources. For example, plants in the Sonoran Desert of Arizona do not usually have to compete for light but do often compete for water, which is a very limited resource most of the year. Other resources plants compete for are nutrients such as nitrogen and phosphorus, and space for growth. In the following experiment, you will see what happens when plants compete for space to grow.

You Will Need

potting soil
10 pots
seeds (check a local nursery or garden shop for seeds that germinate and grow rapidly)
marking pen
ruler

Procedure

1. Place the same amount of potting soil in each of the 10 pots.

2. Plant 3 seeds in each of 5 pots. Label each pot with a 3.

3. Plant 15 seeds in each of the remaining 5 pots. Label each pot with a 15.

4. Randomly place the pots in the same area near a window.

5. Rotate the pots once every day to make sure that some do not receive more sunlight than others.

6. Give the same amount of water to each pot.

7. Allow the seeds to germinate.

8. Once the plants have started to grow, measure the height of each plant.

9. Record the average height of the plants in each pot.

10. Continue to measure the height of the plants once a day for a period of two to three weeks.

Experiment: Competition Among Plants (cont'd.)

Results and Analysis

1. What is the average height of the plants in the pots containing 3 seeds?

_____

2. What is the average height of the plants in the pots containing 15 seeds?

_____

Conclusion

What conclusion can you draw based on your measurements?

_____

_____

_____

Lesson 8 Diversity and Adaptations of Organisms

How many different kinds of organisms can you name? Organisms that may come to mind include dogs, cats, deer, squirrels, frogs, whales, bees, and robins. Across Earth, there are millions of different species. All these organisms point to the biodiversity that exists on Earth. **Biodiversity** is the variety and complexity of life on Earth. This biodiversity ranges from single cell bacteria to complex organisms made of trillions of cells, such as humans. In this lesson, you will learn about the evidence that shows this biodiversity developed gradually over Earth's long history.

Change in the Environment over Time

Scientists estimate that Earth is about 4.5 billion years old. During that time, Earth has changed a great deal. Even today, the environment is constantly changing. In some cases, these changes happen naturally. For example, a volcano may erupt or a hurricane may strike land. If this happens, the landscape is changed. In some cases, the changes can last for a very long time. Organisms that live in the area may have to move to new locations. These organisms include humans who may have to find new homes.

Key Terms

biodiversity—the variety and complexity of life that exists on Earth

mass extinction—a period of time in Earth's history when many species become extinct

evolution—the gradual change in a species over time

fossil—the remains of an organism that has been preserved in the earth

absolute dating—a method used to determine the age of a fossil or rock

half-life—the time it takes for half of the unstable atoms in a sample to decay

Changes to the environment are also caused by humans. Such changes include (1) construction of villages, towns, and cities; (2) pollution of the waters and the land; and (3) the combustion of fossil fuels that releases gases into the atmosphere that may cause global warming.

Organisms that live in a changing environment face two options—survive the changes or move on to a new environment. To survive, an organism needs a characteristic or trait that will improve its chances of living. You learned that a characteristic that helps an organism survive and reproduce in its environment is called an adaptation. An adaptation may be a physical feature. For example, fur is an adaptation that helps an organism to survive the cold weather in certain environments. An adaptation may also be a behavior. An organism may display an aggressive behavior to protect itself from a predator.

Change in Species over Time

In some cases, organisms do not have the adaptations to survive a changing environment. These organisms may also be unable to move to a new environment. If this is the case, then these organisms may become extinct or die out completely. When a species becomes extinct, it does not reappear.

During Earth's long history, several large-scale extinctions have occurred. These periods when many species become extinct are called **mass extinctions.** One example of a mass extinction occurred about 65 million years ago. At that time, all the species of dinosaurs on Earth became extinct. Scientists think that a large meteorite struck Earth and sent up a huge cloud of dust. This dust cloud blanketed Earth and prevented any sunlight from reaching its surface. Without sunlight, plants could not carry out photosynthesis. The plants slowly died, followed by animals, such as the dinosaurs, that depended on the plants for food.

If organisms possess the adaptations to survive a changing environment, then they will live, reproduce, and maintain their species. However, the species will slowly change over time. The process in which a species gradually changes over time is called **evolution.** Scientists continue to debate how evolution occurs. However, they have several pieces of evidence that evolution has taken place. Extinct species represent only one

www.harcourtschoolsupply.com
80
Lesson 8, Diversity and Adaptations of Organisms
Science 6, SV 9781419034343

example. Living species are also evidence that evolution is a process that occurs in nature.

Evidence for Changes over Time

As a rule, changes in a species take a very long time. Therefore, living proof of evolution is difficult to find. However, one well-studied case involves an organism known as the peppered moth. Before the Industrial Revolution in England during the late eighteenth and early nineteenth centuries, almost all the peppered moths were light gray with little black speckled spots. A few moths were completely black.

The light-colored moths were able to blend in with the light-colored tree bark. The less common black moth was more likely to be seen and eaten by birds. Therefore, light color was an adaptation because the light-colored moths were much better at hiding from predators.

At the start of the Industrial Revolution in England, the countryside near London and other cities was blanketed with soot from the new coal-burning factories. As a result, the trees became covered with soot. This was a major change in the environment. Light color was no longer an adaptation. The birds now preyed upon the light-colored moths that were easy to spot on the dark trees. Dark-colored moths, on the other hand, blended in with the trees and were not as easily spotted by the birds.

Although a majority of light-colored moths initially continued to be produced, most of them didn't survive. In contrast, the dark-colored moths flourished. Over the course of many generations of moths, more and more dark-colored moths survived to reproduce. By 1895, the percentage of dark-colored moths was reported at 98 percent, a dramatic change from what it had been before the Industrial Revolution. In modern times, the dark-colored moth is becoming less frequent because of cleaner air standards.

These changes from light color to dark color and then back to light color show that species do change over time. Although this did not happen in the case of the moths, the changes can be so dramatic that a new species is formed. Evidence for the formation of new species comes from a record that has been preserved in the rocks.

Fossils

Earth's surface is made up of layers of rock and soil stacked on top of each other. Sometimes, the remains of a once-living organism are buried in these layers. Over time, these remains become a fossil. A **fossil** is the remains of an organism that has been preserved in the earth. A fossil may be a complete organism, parts of an organism, or just an imprint left by an organism such as a footprint.

By studying fossils, scientists have uncovered a record of life on Earth. The fossil record provides evidence about the order in which organisms have existed. Fossils found in deeper, older layers of Earth may not resemble present-day organisms. However, fossils in upper, newer layers of Earth are similar to present-day organisms. In some cases, scientists have established a fossil record that they think shows the evolution of a modern-day species. The illustrations below show four fossils that scientists think led to the evolution of modern whales.

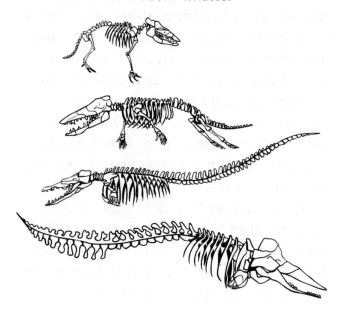

Common Ancestor

The fossil record also shows that groups of organisms share a common ancestor. For example, scientists think that whales and some type of hoofed mammals, such as bison, have a common ancestor based on the fossil record. This ancestor probably lived on land between 50 and 70 million years ago, about the same time as the dinosaurs became extinct. How do scientists determine the age of fossils and estimate when a common ancestor lived? Scientists use a method called absolute dating.

Absolute dating is a method that measures the age of fossils or rocks in years.

To determine the age, scientists examine atoms. Some types of atoms are unstable. These atoms decay to form different types of atoms. Each kind of atom decays at its own rate. This time is measured in a half-life. A **half-life** is the time it takes for half of the unstable atoms in a sample to decay.

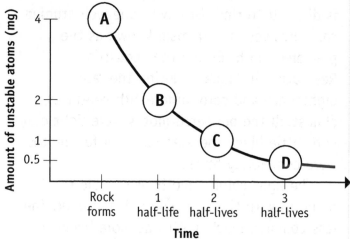

For example, the half-life of an unstable atom known as carbon-14 is 5,730 years. Therefore, if a sample contained 10 grams of carbon-14, then in 5,730 years, there would only be 5 grams of carbon-14 left. The other 5 grams would have decayed to form another, more stable type of atom. By measuring the ratio of unstable atoms to stable atoms, scientists can determine the approximate age of a fossil. Scientists have discovered fossils of bacteria that they think are 3.5 billion years old.

Lesson 8

Review

Darken the circle by the best answer.

1. Dark-colored bodies became an adaptation for peppered moths when the
   - (A) birds no longer fed on them.
   - (B) tree trunks became darkened with soot.
   - (C) Industrial Revolution was over.
   - (D) light-colored moths moved to a different environment.

2. Which part of an organism is most likely to become a fossil?
   - (A) skin
   - (B) blood
   - (C) bone
   - (D) brain

3. Evolution is defined as the
   - (A) pollution of water and land.
   - (B) extinction of organisms.
   - (C) adaptation of organisms.
   - (D) change in a species over time.

4. The absolute age of a fossil is measured by examining
   - (A) unstable atoms that the fossil still contains.
   - (B) where the fossil was found.
   - (C) how deep into the ground the fossil was found.
   - (D) other fossils that are similar.

5. The half-life of an unstable atom is 1,000 years. If a sample contains 10 grams of this unstable atom, what percentage will be left after 2,000 years?
   - (A) 100%
   - (B) 75%
   - (C) 50%
   - (D) 25%

6. Which animal disappeared as a result of a mass extinction?
   - (A) peppered moths
   - (B) whales
   - (C) dinosaurs
   - (D) gorillas

7. What is a common ancestor?

   _____

   _____

   _____

8. How have humans affected biodiversity? Explain your answer.

   _____

   _____

   _____

   _____

Lesson 8   Pangea

In 1912, Alfred Wegener proposed a hypothesis called continental drift. His theory suggests that long ago the continents formed one giant landmass surrounded by a gigantic ocean. Wegener call this landmass *Pangea*, which means "all Earth." Wegener used fossils to support his claim. The map below shows the areas where fossils of certain organisms have been found. Use this map to answer the questions that follow.

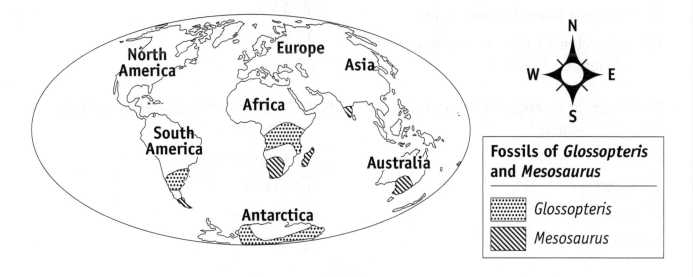

1. On which continents have the fossils of *Mesosaurus* been found?

_____

2. On which continents have the fossils of *Glossopteris* been found?

_____

3. Do these fossil finds support Wegener's theory of *Pangea*? Explain your answer.

_____

_____

_____

Lesson 8

Fossils and Rock Layers

The graph below shows data about fossilized teeth that were found within a series of rock layers. Use this graph to answer the questions that follow. Herbivores are animals that eat plants. Carnivores are animals that eat other animals.

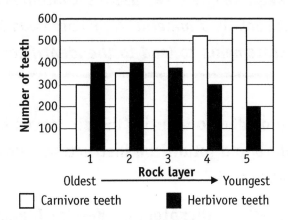

1. What conclusion can you draw about what happened to the number of herbivores over time?

_____

_____

2. What conclusion can you draw about what happened to the number of carnivores over time?

_____

_____

3. Suggest a reason that explains the change that took place in the number of herbivores over time.

_____

_____

4. Suggest a reason that explains the change that took place in the number of carnivores over time.

_____

_____

Lesson 8

Identifying an Organism

Trying to identify an organism can be a difficult task. You could try to compare the organism to those described in a classification system. However, this process can be very time consuming. People often use a dichotomous key to identify an organism or other object such as a mineral. A dichotomous key uses pairs of contrasting descriptive statements to lead to the identification of an organism.

Use the dichotomous key provided to identify the six leaves below. Begin with paired descriptions 1a and 1b and follow the instructions. Proceed through the key until you have identified each leaf.

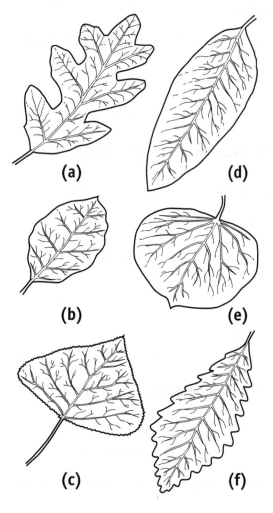

(a)   (d)

(b)   (e)

(c)   (f)

Dichotomous Key for Identifying Common Leaves

1a. If the edge of the leaf has no teeth, or lobes, go to 2 in the key.

1b. If the edge of the leaf has teeth, or lobes, go to 3 in the key.

2a. If the leaf has slightly wavy edges, it is a shingle oak.

2b. If the leaf has smooth edges, go to 4 in the key.

3a. If the leaf edge is toothed, it is a Lombardy poplar.

3b. If the leaf edge has lobes, go to 5 in the key.

4a. If the leaf is heart-shaped with veins branching from the base, it is a redbud.

4b. If the leaf is not heart-shaped, it is a live oak.

5a. If the leaf edge has a few large lobes, it is an English oak.

5b. If the leaf edge has many small lobes, it is a chestnut oak.

(a) _____

(b) _____

(c) _____

(d) _____

(e) _____

(f) _____

Lesson 8

A Chinese Treasure

Read the following passage and then answer the questions that follow the passage.

Between 120 and 145 million years ago, the Liaoning Province in China was dotted with freshwater lakes. However, the area was not a peaceful place. Volcanoes were active. Volcanoes were constantly spewing ash into the air. The ash covered many of the animals, causing their deaths. Some of the animals fell into the lakes, where they quickly sank to the bottom. There they became buried in the sediment at the lake bottom. More and more sediment slowly collected on top of their remains. Without oxygen, their remains did not decompose. Instead, they became fossils.

Normally, only hard parts such as bones and teeth become fossils. Softer body parts decompose. However, the fossil animals in Liaoning Province still had their delicate features because they were buried so quickly and did not decompose. Fossils were found with feathers, fish scales, and wings. One of the most interesting specimens was a fossil of a dinosaur covered from head to tail with downy fluff and primitive feathers. It was the first dinosaur found with its entire body covering intact. The dinosaur fossil was uncovered in 2001 by farmers digging in the area. The dinosaur's skeleton resembles that of a large duck with a big tail and an oversized head.

This dinosaur's fossil supports the theory that modern birds evolved from dinosaurs. Some scientists had thought that dinosaurs did not have true feathers but only feather-like structures. They also suggested that the birds and dinosaurs had simply died in the same place by chance and formed fossils that

were later discovered together. However, discovering a dinosaur fossil covered with feathers demonstrated that birds evolved from dinosaurs. Scientists think that these dinosaurs did not fly. Therefore, this fossil also shows that animals developed feathers for warmth before they could fly.

1. Which characteristic convinced scientists that this dinosaur was an ancestor of modern birds?
   - (A) skeleton like that of a large duck
   - (B) feathers
   - (C) oversized head
   - (D) wings

2. Why did this dinosaur form a fossil that remained intact for millions of years?
   - (A) It was covered with feathers.
   - (B) It had a large head.
   - (C) It was buried immediately and not exposed to oxygen.
   - (D) It could keep warm.

3. Why was this fossil an important discovery?
   - (A) It lived many millions of years ago.
   - (B) It was found in China.
   - (C) It is a dinosaur.
   - (D) It revealed that dinosaurs were an ancestor of modern birds.

Lesson 8

Experiment: Half-Life

Scientists sometimes make models to help them understand the processes that occur in nature. These models can be quite sophisticated and complex. Such models are usually created with a computer. In contrast, some models can be very simple. In the following experiment, pennies will serve as a model to demonstrate the concept of a half-life.

You Will Need

200 pennies
plastic container with lid
clock or watch with second hand
graph paper
ruler
pencil

Procedure

1. Place the pennies in the container and cover.

2. Shake the pennies by turning the container upside down and back up for 15 seconds.

3. Open the container and spill the pennies on a flat surface.

4. Remove all the pennies that are heads up.

5. Count the number of pennies that are left (tails up) and place them back in the container.

6. Repeat steps 2–5 until there are no pennies left to place back in the container.

7. Make a graph of your results. Plot the number of shakes along the horizontal axis and the number of pennies left along the vertical axis.

Experiment: Half-Life (cont'd.)

Results and Analysis

1. What does each penny represent?

_____

2. What does each shake of the container represent?

_____

3. What percent of the pennies is removed after each shake?

_____

Conclusion

What conclusion can you draw based on the results illustrated in your graph?

_____

_____

_____

Lesson 9 Earth's History and Structure

There is something you probably see every day, but you usually do not pay any attention to it. It is a rock. Perhaps there are rocks scattered on the ground. Or you might see a driveway made from small rocks or stones. Maybe you see kitchen countertops made from marble or a walkway made from slate. Both marble and slate are types of rocks. In this lesson, you will learn about rocks and discover that new rock is continually being made in nature from old rock.

Rocks and Minerals

A **rock** is defined as a natural substance that is made of one or more minerals. A **mineral** is a naturally occurring, solid substance that has a crystal structure. In other words, the particles that make up a mineral are arranged in a definite pattern. You may be familiar with several minerals, such as quartz and silica. However, you are probably more familiar with certain minerals known as gemstones. These include diamond, ruby, sapphire, and emerald. All rocks are made of minerals, but minerals are not made of rocks. There are three types of rocks known as igneous, sedimentary, and metamorphic.

Key Terms

rock—a natural substance made of one or more minerals

mineral—a natural, solid substance that has a crystal structure

igneous rock—a rock that forms when hot, liquid rock cools and solidifies

magma—hot, liquid rock

sedimentary rock—a rock that forms from layers of sediment that are compacted and cemented together

metamorphic rock—a rock in which the structure, texture, or composition of the rock has changed

rock cycle—the series of events in which new rock forms from old rock

mechanical weathering—the process where rocks break down into smaller pieces without changing their chemical composition

chemical weathering—the process where rocks break down into smaller pieces as a result of chemical reactions

acid precipitation—rain, sleet, and snow that contains a high level of acids

soil—a substance made up of loose, weathered rock and organic material

Igneous Rocks

Igneous rock forms when hot, liquid rock cools and solidifies. Hot, liquid rock is called **magma**. An igneous rock can form below Earth's surface or above, perhaps around a volcano. When a volcano erupts, magma may flow from it. This magma is known as lava. Lava may also flow from long, narrow cracks in the Earth known as fissures. The amount of lava that flows from a fissure can be large enough to cover the land. When this happens, a lava plateau is formed.

The substances that are trapped in the magma determine the composition, or chemical makeup, of the igneous rock. For example, igneous rocks can be light colored, such as granite, or dark colored, such as basalt. The difference in color depends on the composition of the igneous rock. Granite forms from magma that is rich in the elements sodium, aluminum, potassium, and silicon. These substances do not provide much color. As a result, igneous rocks that contain these substances are light colored. In contrast, basalt forms from magma that is rich in iron, magnesium, and calcium. These substances give basalt its dark color.

The amount of time it takes for the magma to cool determines its texture, or the size and shape of the grains in the rock. Granite and basalt differ not only in their color but also in their texture. Granite forms when magma cools very slowly. As a result, the mineral crystals have more time to grow and get larger. This results in a coarser texture. In contrast, the magma that forms basalt cools much more quickly. This produces smaller crystals and a smoother texture. If magma cools very rapidly, then it contains few or no crystals and is very smooth. The illustration shows that different kinds of igneous rock form when magma cools at different rates.

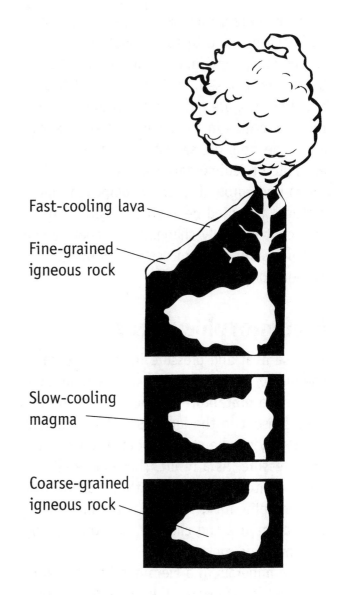

Fast-cooling lava

Fine-grained igneous rock

Slow-cooling magma

Coarse-grained igneous rock

Sedimentary Rocks

Above Earth's surface, wind and water break down rocks into small pieces called sediments. Rock sediment, soil, and the remains of living things can accumulate, become compacted, and slowly become cemented together. **Sedimentary rock** is formed from layers of sediment that are compacted and cemented together.

The most distinctive feature about sedimentary rock is its layers. A single layer of sedimentary rock can extend for several miles. Such formations of sedimentary rock can be seen in the Grand Canyon in Arizona.

Sedimentary rock exists in a variety of compositions and textures. Shale is a sedimentary rock that is smooth and dark. Sandstone is a sedimentary rock that has a coarser texture and is light colored. The rock structures in Monument Valley in Arizona are made from red sandstone. Another example of sedimentary rock is coal. Coal forms underground when decomposed plant material is buried beneath sediment. This sediment is slowly changed into coal by heat and pressure. This process occurs over millions of years.

Metamorphic Rocks

Intense heat and pressure inside Earth can chemically change igneous and sedimentary rocks into **metamorphic rocks**. Minerals that were present in the igneous and sedimentary rocks may not be stable under intense heat and pressure. As a result, these minerals change into different ones that make up the metamorphic rock. Many of these minerals, such as garnet and chlorite, are found only in metamorphic rock.

The minerals in a metamorphic rock are arranged in two ways. The minerals can be arranged in bands, such as slate, or form an irregular arrangement in the rock, such as

marble. Both slate and marble are used in the construction of homes, offices, and public buildings. Marble was used to build the Lincoln Memorial in Washington, DC.

Rock Cycle

If the temperature and pressure are too great, however, rocks will melt. Melted metamorphic rock can form magma that becomes an igneous rock as it cools. Intense heat and pressure can also change sedimentary rock into metamorphic rock. These changes are part of the **rock cycle**, which is illustrated in the following diagram.

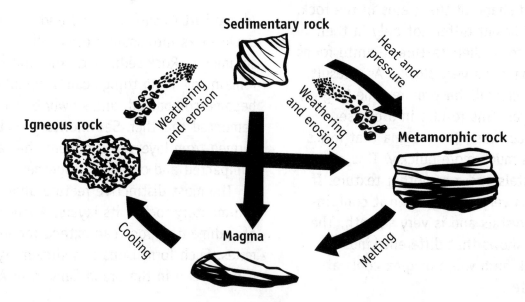

Notice in the diagram on page 92 that the rock cycle involves many pathways. Igneous rock can change into metamorphic rock, sedimentary rock, or even back into igneous rock. Several factors determine which pathway a rock will follow. These factors include time, heat, and pressure. Another factor is the rock's location. A rock deep beneath Earth's surface is mainly affected by heat and pressure. In contrast, a rock on the surface is mainly affected by weathering.

Weathering

Major events such as earthquakes and volcanoes are processes that can suddenly shape Earth's surface. Earth's surface is also changed gradually through other processes. One such process is weathering. As a result of weathering, rocks are broken down into smaller pieces. There are two kinds of weathering: mechanical and chemical.

Mechanical weathering breaks rocks down into smaller pieces without changing their chemical composition. Rocks may be mechanically weathered by ice. Water seeps into cracks in a rock and freezes. As water freezes, it expands and pushes on the rock. Small wedges appear in the rock. Eventually, the pressure from the ice makes the wedges larger so that the rock breaks apart.

Chemical weathering breaks rocks down into smaller pieces as a result of chemical reactions. Unlike mechanical weathering, chemical weathering changes the chemical composition of rocks. Air, water, salts, and acids may react with the minerals in rocks to form new substances. As a result, the rocks are weakened and may break, dissolve, or wash away. Over many years, chemical weathering can destroy statues or carve out enormous caves.

Recently, chemical weathering from precipitation, such as rain and snow, has become a much more significant factor. Precipitation is naturally acidic. However, rain, sleet, and snow can contain a high concentration of acids and is called **acid precipitation**. The high levels of acids in this precipitation can cause very rapid weathering of rocks. Acid precipitation is caused by the burning of fossil fuels, such as coal and oil.

Soil

You may think that weathering is only a damaging force. This is not the case. Weathering produces one of our most precious natural resources—soil. **Soil** is made up of loose, weathered rock and organic material. Organic material comes from the remains of living things.

The formation of soil begins with rock or materials deposited by winds, rivers, and ice. Soil forms as the rock or materials are gradually weathered over time. Mature soil generally forms in layers. The top layer is known as topsoil. Topsoil is darker than soil in the other layers because it contains organic material, or *humus*. Humus forms from decayed organic matter such as bacteria, earthworms, plants, and other organisms. Good topsoil is necessary for growing flowering plants and crops.

www.harcourtschoolsupply.com
93
Lesson 9, Earth's History and Structure
Science 6, SV 9781419034343

Lesson 9   Review

Darken the circle by the best answer.

1. Which process is an example of the chemical weathering of rock?

   Ⓐ Mosses wedge their roots into crevices in a rock, pushing it apart.

   Ⓑ Carbonic acid dissolves rocks to hollow out underground caverns.

   Ⓒ Rocks and rock fragments are pulled by gravity to the bottom of a mountain.

   Ⓓ Water flowing in a river digs out a canyon over millions of years.

2. Which is the most noticeable feature about sedimentary rock?

   Ⓐ large crystals

   Ⓑ rough texture

   Ⓒ layered structure

   Ⓓ dark color

3. Hot, liquid rock is called

   Ⓐ magma.

   Ⓑ igneous rock.

   Ⓒ weathered rock.

   Ⓓ soil.

4. Rhyolite is an igneous rock that contains very fine grains. Therefore, rhyolite

   Ⓐ forms from magma that cools very slowly.

   Ⓑ forms from magma that cools very quickly.

   Ⓒ contains layers.

   Ⓓ is a hot, liquid rock.

5. Which of the following can cause the chemical weathering of rocks?

   Ⓐ pressure

   Ⓑ breakage

   Ⓒ erosion

   Ⓓ acid precipitation

6. Which is a metamorphic rock?

   Ⓐ diamond

   Ⓑ basalt

   Ⓒ marble

   Ⓓ sandstone

7. Explain why fossils of dead organisms are not usually found in metamorphic rock.

   _____

   _____

   _____

   _____

Lesson 9

The Rock Cycle

Use the following diagram to answer the questions that follow.

1. What two factors are required to form metamorphic rock?

   _____

2. What two processes affect rocks at the surface of Earth?

   _____

3. What does the arrow that curves away from and back to metamorphic rocks indicate?

   _____

   _____

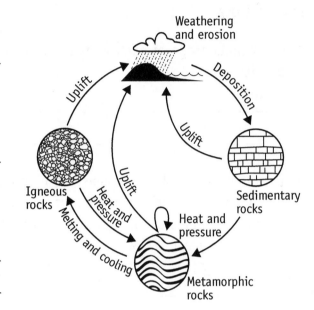

4. What is meant by the term *deposition*?

   _____

   _____

5. What is meant by the term *uplift*?

   _____

   _____

Lesson 9

The Composition of a Rock

The bar graph below shows the percentage of minerals by mass in a sample of granite, which is an igneous rock. Use this graph to answer the questions that follow.

1. What percentage of each mineral makes up granite?

   _____

   _____

2. If a granite sample has a mass of 10 grams, how many grams of quartz does it contain? How many grams of biotite does it contain?

   _____

   _____

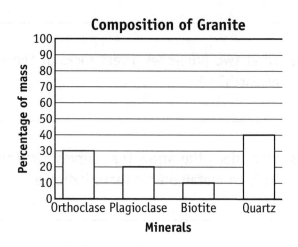

3. Plagioclase is the most common mineral in igneous rocks. Does the graph above support this statement? Explain your answer.

   _____

   _____

4. Both plagioclase and orthoclase are known as feldspar minerals. What percentage of this granite sample consists of minerals that are not feldspar minerals?

   _____

   _____

Lesson 9   Chemical Weathering

The graph below shows the average yearly rainfall in five locations. Use this graph to answer the questions that follow.

1. At which location would you expect to find the most chemical weathering? Explain your answer.

_____

_____

2. At which location would you expect to find the least amount of chemical weathering? Explain your answer.

_____

_____

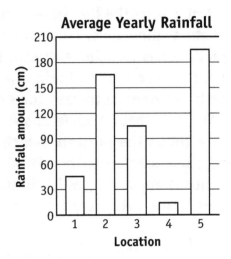

Average Yearly Rainfall

3. How would the rocks be affected by mechanical weathering in these two locations? Explain your answer.

_____

_____

www.harcourtschoolsupply.com   97   Lesson 9, Chemical Weathering
Science 6, SV 9781419034343

Lesson 9

Experiment: Acid Precipitation

Some areas of the country are more affected by acid rain than other areas are. These areas are usually located near industrial centers where the burning of fossil fuels can increase the acidity of the precipitation. The effects of this acid precipitation can be neutralized by the limestone found in lake bottoms and in the soil. Some areas have a lot of natural limestone. Crushed limestone is sometimes added to lakes, ponds, and other aquatic areas to help neutralize the effects of acid rain. This is done to save organisms until the source of acid rain can be reduced. In the following experiment, you can check how limestone neutralizes the effect of acid precipitation.

You will check a value known as pH to determine the level of acidity. The illustration below shows the pH scale, which ranges from 0 to 14. The lower the pH value is, the more acidic the substance. The pH values of common substances are shown. Notice that the pH of milk is about 6.5, which is slightly acidic. Vinegar is more acidic with a pH value of about 3. The pH of ammonia is about 12, indicating that it is not acidic but alkaline.

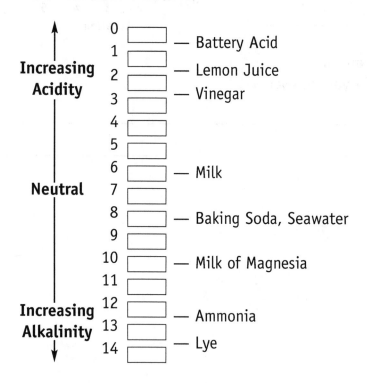

Experiment: Acid Precipitation (cont'd.)

You Will Need

masking tape
marker
two soup bowls
measuring cup
crushed limestone (available at a garden center)
teaspoon
white vinegar
distilled water (available at a pharmacy)
spoons
garden soil pH testing kit
baking soda
plastic wrap
notebook and pencil

Procedure

1. Label one bowl "vinegar" and the other bowl "vinegar/limestone."

2. Add $\frac{1}{4}$ cup of crushed limestone into the bowl labeled "vinegar/limestone."

3. Pour 1 teaspoon of vinegar into 2 cups of distilled water, stir well, and check the pH using a garden soil pH testing kit. The pH of the vinegar/water mixture should be about 4. If it is below pH 4, add a sprinkle of baking soda, stir well, and recheck the pH. If the pH is above 4, add a drop or two of vinegar and again recheck the pH.

4. Pour about 1 cup of the vinegar/water mixture over the limestone in the bowl and stir with a clean, dry spoon.

5. Pour the remaining vinegar/water mixture into the other bowl.

6. Check the pH of the vinegar/water mixture in the bowl with the limestone and record this value.

7. Cover each bowl with plastic wrap to prevent evaporation.

8. Every day for 6 days, stir the contents of each bowl with a clean, dry spoon. When the limestone has settled (about 4 or more hours later), test the pH of the water mixture in each bowl and record the results.

Experiment: Acid Precipitation (cont'd.)

Results and Analysis

1. Did the pH of the vinegar/water mixture in the bowl with limestone become more or less acidic during the 6-day period? If so, how did it change?

_____

_____

2. Did the pH of the vinegar/water mixture in the bowl without limestone change during the 6-day period?

_____

Conclusion

What conclusion can you draw based on your observations?

_____

_____

_____

Lesson 10 Earth in the Solar System

In 1543, our concept of the solar system was totally changed. That year, a Polish scientist named Nicolas Copernicus published a book in which he said that the sun was the center of our solar system. At that time, scientists knew that there were six planets. These planets included Mercury, Venus, Earth, Mars, Jupiter, and Saturn. Before Copernicus, scientists thought that Earth was the center of our solar system. The other five planets and the sun were believed to orbit Earth. Copernicus said that all the planets, including Earth, orbited the sun. This view of our solar system would remain unchanged for almost 250 years.

The Nine(?) Planets

In 1781, an English scientist named William Hershel discovered a seventh planet by studying the night sky with his telescope. This was Uranus. In 1846, still another planet was discovered. This was Neptune. Finally, in 1930, Pluto was added as the ninth planet in our solar system. In 2006, however, an international group of scientists decided that Pluto did not meet the definition of a planet.

The Inner Planets

Mercury, Venus, Earth, and Mars are known as inner planets because they are closer to the sun. Mercury is the closest planet to the sun. Mercury's period of revolution is 88 days. The **period of revolution** is the time it takes for an object to revolve around the sun once. Mercury's period of rotation is 58 days and 19 hours. The **period of rotation** is the time it takes for an object to rotate or spin around once. Because of its slow rotation, a day on Mercury is almost 59 Earth days long. However, because of its rapid revolution, a year on Mercury is only 88 Earth days long.

Key Terms

period of revolution—the time it takes for an object to revolve around the sun once

period of rotation—the time it takes for an object to rotate once

retrograde rotation—the clockwise spin of a planet as seen from above its North Pole

astronomical unit (AU)—the average distance between the sun and Earth

gas giant—one of the four large, outer planets made mostly of gases

www.harcourtschoolsupply.com
101
Lesson 10, Earth in the Solar System
Science 6, SV 9781419034343

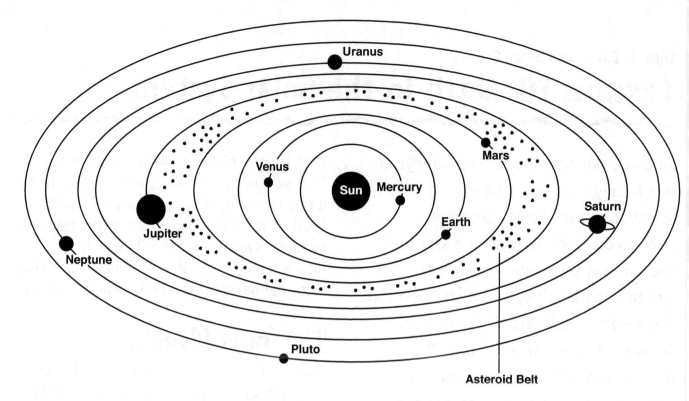

Venus is more like Earth than any other planet. Venus is about the same size and has about the same density as Earth. In some ways, Venus is very different from Earth. Earth's atmosphere is mostly nitrogen and oxygen. Venus's atmosphere is mostly carbon dioxide. Carbon dioxide traps heat energy from the sun. As a result, Venus's surface temperature can reach almost 870°F. This makes the surface temperature of Venus the hottest of any planet.

Unlike what happens on Earth, the sun on Venus rises in the west and sets in the east. The reason is that Venus and Earth rotate in opposite directions. If viewed from its North Pole, Earth rotates in a counterclockwise direction. If viewed from its North Pole, Venus rotates in a clockwise direction. This is known as a **retrograde rotation.**

Earth is the only planet known to support life. Life is possible because of water. Water is a vital part of the chemical processes that living things depend on for survival. When the planets formed about five billion years ago, Earth formed at just the right distance from the sun. Earth was not too close so that the temperature would be too high, and water would boil away. Earth was also not too far so that the temperature would be too low, and water would freeze.

Mars is a cold planet where the temperature may not get above freezing even during its summer months. A day on Mars is about 1 Earth day long. However, a year on Mars is almost 2 Earth years long. Several spacecraft have landed on Mars, beginning with *Viking I* in 1976. These spacecraft have gathered data that indicate Mars once had liquid water. Perhaps Mars once was a warmer planet. Mars is also home to the largest mountain in the solar system. This mountain is called Olympus Mons. The base of Olympus Mons is as large as Arizona. It rises about 88,600 feet, or three times as high as Mount Everest. The following table compares the inner planets.

The Inner Planets

Planet	Distance from sun (AU)	Diameter (miles)	Period of revolution	Period of rotation
Mercury	0.39	3,032	88 days	58 days, 19 hours
Venus	0.72	7,521	224 days, 17 hours	243 days, 6 hours
Earth	1	7,936	365 days, 6 hours	23 hours, 56 minutes
Mars	1.5	4,222	1 year, 322 days	24 hours, 40 minutes

Notice that the distance from the sun has the unit AU. This stands for **astronomical unit**. The average distance from the sun to Earth is set as 1 AU. This is about 93 million miles. The distance from the sun to Mars is about 140 million miles (1.5 AU × 93 million miles). Distances in the solar system can also be measured using the speed of light as a reference. Light travels at around 186,000 miles per second. In 1 minute, light travels 11,160,000 miles. Light takes 8.3 minutes to travel from the sun to Earth. So, the distance between the sun and Earth can be given either as 1 AU or 8.3 light-minutes.

The Outer Planets

Jupiter, Saturn, Uranus, and Neptune are known as the outer planets because they are farther from the sun. These planets also share certain features. They are very large and made mostly of gases. For this reason, they are referred to as gas giants. A **gas giant** is a planet that is made mostly of gases rather than the rocky materials of the inner planets.

Jupiter is the largest planet in our solar system. Like the sun, Jupiter is made mostly of hydrogen and helium gases. The interior of Jupiter is extremely hot. As a result, Jupiter radiates more heat energy into space than it receives from the sun. Jupiter is also home to the Great Red Spot, which is a storm system that is similar to a hurricane on Earth. However, there are some major differences.

The Great Red Spot has lasted for at least 400 years, or for as long as humans have observed it through telescopes from Earth. In addition, the storm is immense. Three planets the size of Earth would fit within the Great Red Spot. The storm is centered in Jupiter's southern hemisphere. However, it rotates in a counterclockwise direction, opposite to the way a hurricane rotates in the southern hemisphere on Earth.

Saturn is the second-largest planet in the solar system. Like Jupiter, Saturn is made mostly of hydrogen and helium gases. All the gas giants are surrounded by rings. However, Saturn's are the largest and probably best known. The rings are made of ice particles that range in size from a few inches to several meters wide. The total diameter of the rings is almost 170,000 miles or more than 20 times Earth's diameter.

Compared to Saturn, Uranus is twice as far from Earth. Nonetheless, you can still pick Uranus out from among the hundreds of stars that you would also see. However, you need excellent eyesight, know just where to look in the night sky, and stare very hard to find it. Like Venus, Uranus has a retrograde rotation. Uranus is also a world on its side. Uranus has a tilt of almost 98 degrees. A tilt of 90 degrees is a quarter turn. Some scientists think that Uranus's tilt was the result of a collision with a massive object that caused the planet to turn on its side.

Because of its tilt, its north pole is sometimes almost directly in line with the sun. At this point, Uranus's northern hemisphere is entirely in sunlight. Uranus takes about 84 Earth years to complete one orbit around the sun. As a result, its north pole will be in sunlight for some 21 Earth years. During this time, its southern hemisphere will be in complete darkness.

Most of what we know of Neptune comes from *Voyager 2*, a spacecraft that visited the planet in 1989. Neptune emits a bluish color. Like Jupiter and Saturn, Neptune emits more heat energy into space than it receives from the sun. Neptune is also home to the Great Dark Spot. *Voyager 2* spotted this giant storm in Neptune's southern hemisphere. The spacecraft recorded wind speeds of 1500 miles per hour, the strongest on any planet. In 1994, the Hubble Space Telescope focused on Neptune only to discover that the Great Dark Spot had vanished. However, it located another Great Dark Spot, but this time in Neptune's northern hemisphere. Neptune seems to be a violent world.

In January 2006, NASA launched a rocket to send a spacecraft on its way to Pluto. The spacecraft is scheduled to fly by Pluto and its tiny moon called Charon in 2015. However, seven months after NASA launched the spacecraft to Pluto, scientists decided that Pluto does not meet the new definition of a planet. To be classified as a planet, a celestial body must not cross the orbit of another body as it travels around the sun. Pluto's orbit crosses that of Neptune. As a result, Pluto has been reclassified in a new category of "dwarf planets." Other "dwarf planets" include Ceres, which was considered a planet in the 1800s, and UB313, which was discovered in 2003.

The following table compares the outer planets.

The Outer Planets

Planet	Distance from sun (AU)	Diameter (miles)	Period of revolution	Period of rotation
Jupiter	5.2	88,846	11 years, 313 days	9 hours, 54 minutes
Saturn	9.6	74,898	29 years, 155 days	10 hours, 42 minutes
Uranus	19.2	31,763	83 years, 273 days	17 hours, 12 minutes
Neptune	30.1	30,775	163 years, 263 days	16 hours, 6 minutes

Name _____ DATE _____

Lesson 10   Review

Darken the circle by the best answer.

1. Which two planets have a retrograde rotation?
   - Ⓐ Venus and Mars
   - Ⓑ Earth and Mercury
   - Ⓒ Uranus and Venus
   - Ⓓ Jupiter and Saturn

2. Which is the largest planet?
   - Ⓐ Jupiter
   - Ⓑ Saturn
   - Ⓒ Earth
   - Ⓓ Uranus

3. Which planet is tilted on its side?
   - Ⓐ Venus
   - Ⓑ Saturn
   - Ⓒ Mars
   - Ⓓ Uranus

4. Which celestial body is considered a "dwarf planet"?
   - Ⓐ Saturn
   - Ⓑ Uranus
   - Ⓒ Pluto
   - Ⓓ Jupiter

5. If an object in space is 2 AUs from the sun, then this object is
   - Ⓐ twice as far than Earth from the sun.
   - Ⓑ twice as close as Earth to the sun.
   - Ⓒ 2 light-minutes from the sun.
   - Ⓓ the closest object in space to the sun.

6. Where is the Great Red Spot located?
   - Ⓐ Mars
   - Ⓑ Jupiter
   - Ⓒ Mercury
   - Ⓓ Saturn

7. How far will light travel through the solar system in 30 seconds? _____

8. What conclusions can you draw about the planets by knowing how far they are from the sun?

_____

_____

9. Why is Pluto no longer classified as a planet?

_____

_____

Lesson 10

The Inner Planets

Use the table below to answer the questions that follow.

The Inner Planets

Planet	Distance from sun (AU)	Diameter (miles)	Period of revolution	Period of rotation
Mercury	0.39	3,032	88 days	58 days, 19 hours
Venus	0.72	7,521	224 days, 17 hours	243 days, 6 hours
Earth	1	7,936	365 days, 6 hours	23 hours, 56 minutes
Mars	1.5	4,222	1 year, 322 days	24 hours, 40 minutes

1. Arrange these planets in order of decreasing size.

_____

2. Does a short period of rotation mean that a planet also has a short period of revolution? Explain your answer.

_____

_____

3. If Earth is 93 million miles from the sun, how far in miles is Venus from the sun?

_____

4. If 1 AU equals 8.3 light-minutes, how far in light-minutes is Mars from the sun?

_____

5. How many times does Mercury rotate during one revolution around the sun?

_____

Lesson 10

The Outer Planets

Use the table below to answer the questions that follow.

The Outer Planets

Planet	Distance from sun (AU)	Diameter (miles)	Period of revolution	Period of rotation
Jupiter	5.2	88,846	11 years, 313 days	9 hours, 54 minutes
Saturn	9.6	74,898	29 years, 155 days	10 hours, 42 minutes
Uranus	19.2	31,763	83 years, 273 days	17 hours, 12 minutes
Neptune	30.1	30,775	163 years, 263 days	16 hours, 6 minutes

1. Arrange these planets in order of increasing size.

_____

2. If Earth is 93 million miles from the sun, how far in miles is Neptune from the sun?

_____

3. If 1 AU equals 8.3 light-minutes, how far in light-minutes is Saturn from the sun?

_____

4. How far is Uranus from the sun in light-hours?

_____

5. How many times does Jupiter revolve around the sun for one revolution that Neptune completes?

_____

Lesson 10

Comparing Planets

The ratio of the mass of a substance to its volume is called density. For example, if a substance has a mass of 4 grams (g) and occupies a volume of 2 cubic centimeters (cm^3), then its density equals 4 g/2 cm^3 or 2 g/cm^3. The graph below shows density versus mass for Earth (E), Uranus (U), and Neptune (N). The relative mass of each planet is given in Earth masses. Earth is given a mass of 1 Earth mass. The relative volumes for the planets are shown by the size of each circle. Use the graph below to answer the questions that follow.

1. Compare the volumes of the three planets.

_____

_____

2. Compare the masses of the three planets.

_____

_____

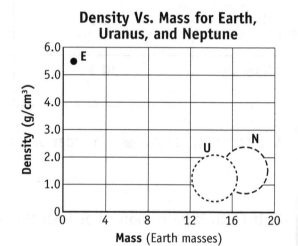

3. Although Earth has the smallest mass, it has the highest density of the three planets. How can Earth be the densest of the three when Uranus and Neptune have so much more mass than Earth does?

_____

_____

Lesson 10   Naming a Planet

Read the following passage and then answer the questions.

As its discoverer, William Herschel was given the honor of naming the new planet he had spotted through his telescope in 1781. He proposed naming the new planet after King George III of England, which was Herschel's adopted homeland. This name, however, was not acceptable to other scientists, especially those living outside England. Moreover, scientists pointed out that tradition called for naming planets after figures in Roman and Greek mythology.

Several scientists proposed a name that made sense. Jupiter was named after the king of the Roman gods. Saturn was named after Jupiter's father. Why not name this new planet after Saturn's father, who was the god of the heavens? In Greek myths, Saturn's father was Ouranos. The Latin spelling for this Greek god is Uranus. The planet Herschel had discovered got its name. However, for the rest of his life, Herschel referred to this new planet as Georgium Sidus, which is Latin for George's Star.

Clyde Tombaugh, who discovered Pluto in 1930, wanted to name the planet Minerva, who was the Roman goddess of wisdom. However, this name had already been given to one of the asteroids, which are huge rocks left over from the formation of our solar system some 4.6 billion years ago. Unable to name the planet Minerva, Tombaugh came across a suggestion sent to him by an eleven-year-old girl living in England. She suggested the name Pluto, after the Greek god of the underworld. Pluto was also the brother of Jupiter and Neptune and a son of Saturn. Tombaugh thought that the name Pluto was most appropriate.

1. How is the god Uranus related to the gods Pluto, Jupiter, and Neptune?

_____

_____

2. In chemistry, elements have been named after famous people. Why wasn't a planet named after the person who first discovered it?

_____

_____

_____

_____

3. Did either Herschel or Tombaugh have anything to do with the names of the planets they discovered? Explain your answer.

_____

_____

_____

_____

Lesson 10

Experiment: Density

The inner planets, which are rocky, have a greater density than the outer planets, which are made of gases. The density of the inner planets ranges between 3.93 g/cm³ for Mars to 5.52 g/cm³ for Earth. In contrast, the densities of the outer planets range between 0.69 g/cm³ for Saturn to 1.64 g/cm³ for Neptune. As a comparison, the density of water is 1.00 g/cm³. An object that has a density greater than water's will sink in water. An object that has a density less than water's will float. This does not mean that a heavy object will always sink, while a light object will always float. You learned that density depends not only on mass but also on volume, as you will see in the following experiment.

You Will Need

adult helper
bathroom scale
bowling ball that weighs 10 pounds or less (about 8 pounds works best)
calculator
string
scissors
yardstick
bathtub

Procedure

1. Have the adult helper weigh himself or herself on the scale.

2. While holding the bowling ball, have the adult helper weigh himself or herself again.

3. Subtract the weight in step 1 from the weight in step 2. This value is the weight of the bowling ball in pounds. Multiply this value by 453.6 grams to convert pounds to grams, the metric value for mass. Record the mass of the bowling ball in grams.

4. Wrap a piece of string around the widest part of the bowling ball. Cut the string and then lay it straight along the yardstick. The length of the string represents the circumference of the bowling ball. According to the official rules, a bowling ball must have a circumference between 26.704 inches and 27.002 inches, so the value you get should be close to 27 inches. Multiply the circumference value by 2.54 to convert inches to centimeters.

Experiment: Density (cont'd.)

5. Calculate the radius of the bowling ball by using the following equation.

$$\text{radius} = \frac{\text{circumference (from step 4)}}{6.28}$$

6. Calculate the volume of the bowling ball by using the following equation.

$$\text{volume} = \frac{4}{3} \times 3.14 \times \text{radius cubed (Notice that the radius must be cubed.)}$$

7. Divide the mass of the bowling ball from step 3 by the volume of the bowling ball from step 6. This value represents the density of the bowling ball in g/cm^3.

8. Predict whether the bowling ball will sink or float.

9. Test your prediction by gently placing the bowling ball in a bathtub full of water.

Results and Analysis

What happens to the bowling ball?

_____

Conclusion

What conclusion can you draw based upon your observations?

_____

_____

Lesson 10, Experiment: Density
Science 6, SV 9781419034343

Science Fair Projects

Although it is at the end of the lesson, each experiment in this book should be the beginning for learning something about science. For example, you may have done the experiment titled *Taking Out the Green*. You may have isolated several different pigments from the spinach leaves. But you can also experiment with other green vegetables to see if you get the same pigments. You can also try extracting the pigments from other colored substances, such as red cabbage and yellow squash. The process used to separate the pigments is called chromatography. You can do some research to see what else can be isolated with the help of chromatography. In other words, you should be creative, like any good scientist.

Designing an Experiment

If you design your own experiment, be sure that you do so safely and correctly. You must carry out all your work with the supervision of an adult, either your parent or teacher. The adult must help with any procedure that involves a risk. For example, the experiment may require the use of a sharp knife or hot stove. The adult should perform these steps. In addition, you must have an adult review the materials you will use and the procedure you will follow *before* you begin any experiment or science fair project.

Also be sure that your experiment has been designed correctly. Whenever a scientist designs an experiment, he or she always includes a control. A control is set up so that only one factor or variable is present in the experiment.

A variable is anything that changes.

For example, you may have done the experiment titled *Competition Among Plants*. The experiment is designed to determine if plants compete for space to grow. Half the pots contained 3 seeds each, while the other half contained 15 seeds each. All the pots were then treated in the same way. They received the same amount of light and water. If the plants grew taller in the pots with only 3 seeds, then you can conclude that competition for space limited the growth in the other pots. In this experiment, the only variable was the number of seeds planted in the pots. No other factor was introduced into the experiment.

Choosing a Project

Any experiment in this book can serve as the basis for a science fair project. Usually, doing a science fair project is a bit more involved than carrying out an experiment. Rather than use an experiment in this book as your starting point, you may want to pick your own topic to investigate. If you do, you will have to do some research to learn something about the topic. This research can involve checking the Internet, reading books, and talking to teachers and scientists. A good place to begin is to think about what you like. For example, if you like building models, then you may want to build a model that explains a scientific principle or concept. Models were used in Lesson 6 to explain how substances get into and out of cells. You can build a model to show what happens as a

www.harcourtschoolsupply.com
112
Science Fair Projects
Science 6, SV 9781419034343

result of diffusion, osmosis, and active transport.

Deciding what to do for a science fair project is often the hardest part of the project. If you have trouble choosing a project, then here are some ideas from each lesson in this book. These ideas will get you started. However, you will have to obtain more information to carry out the project. You can get this information from the Internet, the library, or your teachers. You can also check companies that sell to individuals for items that can help you with your project.

Lesson 1 Properties and Changes of Properties in Matter

- **Chemical Reactions**—Experiment with ways of changing the rate of a chemical reaction. Factors you can test include changing the temperature and the concentration of the reactants. You can also determine what happens when substances known as catalysts are added.
- **Physical Changes**—Measure the temperature as a solid melts and as a liquid freezes. You can use ice cubes and a candle. Be sure to continue heating after the ice cubes have completely melted and continue freezing after the water has completely frozen. Plot the melting and cooling curves for water.
- **Density**—The ratio of a substance's mass to its volume is called its density. Calculate the density of various objects. Relate each substance's density to its ability to float in water. Explain how the density of water changes as it turns from a solid to a liquid and then to a gas.

Lesson 2 Motions and Forces

- **Friction**—Test various methods to increase and reduce friction. Time how long it takes an object to roll down an inclined board. Cover the board with different materials to check how they affect friction.
- **Forces**—Demonstrate how an object will move only if an unbalanced force is applied. Measure the forces applied to an object. To measure the force, you will need to construct a device from rubber bands and a ruler.
- **Bernoulli's Principle**—The Venturi tube is a practical application of Bernoulli's Principle. Build a model of a Venturi tube and explain how it operates. Include information on how these tubes are used in various devices such as barbecue grills.

Lesson 3 Transfer of Energy

- **Kinetic Energy**—Calculate the kinetic energy of various moving objects. The formula for calculating kinetic energy requires that you know both their mass and velocity.
- **Potential Energy**—Calculate the potential energy that is stored in a food such as a peanut. You will have to build a calorimeter and measure the temperature change of a sample of water as the food burns.
- **Electrical Energy**—Demonstrate the difference between a parallel circuit and a series circuit. Include one or more switches in your circuit to demonstrate the difference between open and closed circuits. Use a voltmeter to measure the voltage at various points in each circuit.

Lesson 4 Structure and Function in Living Systems

- **The Cell**—Make a three-dimensional model of the cell showing the various structures it contains. Distinguish between those structures found in an animal cell and those present in a plant cell.
- **Cell Wall**—Demonstrate how a cell wall helps to maintain the rigidity of a plant. Use a microscope to show what happens to both the cell membrane and cell wall when a freshwater plant called elodea is placed in salt water. Include an explanation of turgor pressure.
- **DNA**—The genetic information is stored in the nucleus in a molecule called DNA. Extract or take out the DNA from various cells including spinach, broccoli, and chicken liver. Show what DNA looks like. A detergent is needed. Experiment to find out which detergent works best.

Lesson 5 Reproduction and Heredity

- **Mitosis**—All the stages of mitosis can be observed in the cells found in the tip of an onion root. Prepare slides of onion root tip and identify each stage with the use of a microscope. Use a camera to photograph each stage. You can also calculate the length of time each stage takes.
- **Meiosis**—A process called crossing over occurs during meiosis. Demonstrate how this process occurs and what role it plays in sexual reproduction. You can also describe how scientists have used crossing over to map genes on a chromosome.

- **DNA**—The structure of DNA is called a double helix. Make a model of DNA. Show how DNA is copied in a process called replication before mitosis and meiosis occur.

Lesson 6 Regulation and Behavior

- **Diffusion and Osmosis**—These are two processes by which substances, such as water, enter and leave the cell. Demonstrate what happens as a result of diffusion and osmosis using a freshwater plant known as elodea. Experiment with ways of changing the rate at which these processes occur.
- **Homeostasis**—Use a paramecium to demonstrate how its contractile vacuole maintains homeostasis. The rate at which the vacuole expels water will change depending on the water concentration in its environment. Time how many times the vacuole fills and then expels water under different conditions. This project will require patient observations with a microscope.
- **Dialysis**—Use dialysis tubing to demonstrate how a dialysis machine operates to filter the blood. Dialysis machines are used to treat people with severe kidney problems. Explain how the kidney filters the blood.

Lesson 7 Populations and Ecosystems

- **Ecosystem**—Set up a self-sustaining ecosystem in an aquarium tank. Such a system does not require anything to be added or removed. As a result, you will need producers, consumers, and decomposers. Explain the role of each organism in your ecosystem.

- **Adaptations**—Show how adaptations play a role in evolution. You can either report on an example such as the peppered moth or carry out experiments showing how resistance to antibiotics can evolve in bacteria. You will have to learn how to culture bacteria and take special precautions to prevent any contact with the bacteria.
- **Predators**—Use owl pellets to identify an owl's prey. These pellets contain undigested materials from an owl's diet. Resources will be needed to identify the source of the remains that include bone fragments and hair.

Lesson 8 Diversity and Adaptations of Organisms

- **Fossils**—Make your own fossil prints from specimens such as seashells and chicken bones. Demonstrate the difference between a cast and a mold. Prepare your own molds and casts.
- **Cladograms**—The evolutionary history of different species is sometimes illustrated with a cladogram. Prepare one or more cladograms to show evolutionary relationships. You will have to check the various styles that are used to draw a cladogram. Be sure to use one that is easy to follow.
- **Half-Life**—Develop a model that uses something other than coins to demonstrate the concept of a half-life. Possibilities include candies and playing cards.

Lesson 9 Earth's History and Structure

- **Minerals**—Demonstrate how minerals are identified using various tests, including color, luster, streak, cleavage, hardness, and chemical reactivity. Ask someone to identify an unknown mineral by using a table of information you have prepared.
- **Soils**—Investigate how quickly water seeps through various soil samples in your local area. Obtain samples from gardens, wooded lots, and grassy areas. Include information on groundwater recharge.
- **Rocks**—Use a soda bottle to construct a model to show how sedimentary rock forms. Use cement, sand, plaster, and water to make other types of rocks. Include a description of the rock cycle.

Lesson 10 Earth in the Solar System

- **Measuring Distances in Space**—Build a solar-distance measuring device to calculate how far the sun is from Earth. You can find everything you need right at home. The math involved is simple.
- **Telescope**—This device has provided much information about our solar system. Construct a simple telescope. Use it to make observations of objects in the sky. Prepare a report summarizing your observations.
- **Planetary Motion**—A German scientist named Johannes Kepler described the motion of the planets in three laws. Prepare a report summarizing Kepler's laws. Make a computer animation of a planet's orbit.

Presenting Your Project

Students usually present their projects in the form of a three-sided display. This display should include all the important information about your project. The left side of the display can include any background information you obtained from the Internet, books, or people. You can also place the purpose and procedure of your project on this side.

The center panel on your display should include the title of your project, your name, and grade at the top. All your results should be shown on this center panel. Do not display your results simply by showing what you wrote. Rather try to present them in a more appealing manner. Include photographs, drawings, graphs, and any other visual materials that will help show what you found.

The right side of the display usually includes your conclusion and explanation. Your display will also be more impressive if you include the setup you used in your project or any models that you built. These items are usually displayed on the tabletop in front of the display.

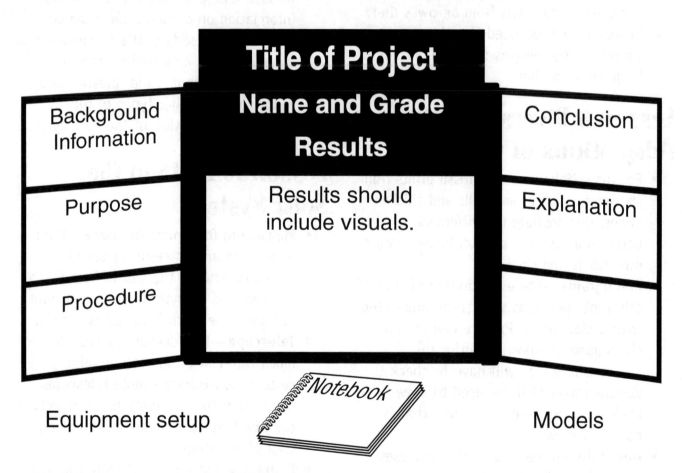

When it is time to present your project, take your time in explaining what you did. Start with the information displayed on the left panel, then move on to the center panel, and then finally review what is shown on the right hand panel. Be sure to impress your listener with what you learned and how much fun you had while doing your science fair project.

Science Fair Projects
Science 6, SV 9781419034343

Glossary

absolute dating—a method used to determine the age of a fossil or rock (p. 79)

acid precipitation—rain, sleet, or snow that contains a high level of acids (p. 90)

active transport—the movement of particles with the use of energy (p. 59)

adaptation—a feature that increases an organism's chance to survive and reproduce (p. 68)

alveolus—a tiny air sac in the lung (p. 59)

Archimedes' principle—principle that states that buoyancy on an object in a fluid is an upward force that equals the weight of the fluid that the object displaces (p. 17)

astronomical unit (AU)—the average distance between the sun and Earth (p. 101)

atmospheric pressure—the pressure caused by the weight of the atmosphere (p. 17)

atom—the basic building block of matter (p. 29)

Bernoulli's principle—principle that states that as the speed of a moving fluid increases, its pressure decreases (p. 17)

biodiversity—the variety and complexity of life that exists on Earth (p. 79)

buoyancy—an upward force that fluids exert on all matter (p. 17)

capillary—a tiny blood vessel (p. 59)

cell—the smallest unit that can carry out all processes necessary for life (p. 40)

cell cycle—the life cycle of a cell (p. 49)

cell membrane—organelle that covers a cell's surface and controls what enters and leaves a cell (p. 40)

cell wall—a rigid structure that supports a plant cell (p. 40)

chemical change—a change that occurs when one or more substances are changed into new substances that have different properties (p. 7)

chemical equation—a way to represent a chemical reaction using chemical symbols and numbers (p. 7)

chemical formula—a combination of chemical symbols and numbers to represent a substance (p. 7)

chemical property—a property that allows matter to be changed into new matter that has different properties (p. 7)

chemical reaction—a process in which one or more substances change to make one or more new substances (p. 7)

chemical weathering—the process where rocks break down into smaller pieces as a result of chemical reactions (p. 90)

chloroplast—organelle where a plant cell makes food (p. 40)

chromosome—the cell structure that stores the hereditary information (p. 49)

commensalism—a symbiotic relationship where one organism benefits and the other organism is not affected in any way (p. 68)

competition—the interaction between two organisms trying to use the same natural resources (p. 68)

conduction—the transfer of heat energy between two objects that are in direct contact (p. 29)

contractile vacuole—an organelle that maintain water balance in unicellular organisms (p. 59)

convection—the transfer of heat energy as the particles in a liquid or gas move (p. 29)

cytokinesis—the division of the cytoplasm of a cell (p. 49)

DNA—the chemical substance that controls the structure and function of cells (p. 49)

daughter cell—a cell produced by the division of a parent cell (p. 49)

decomposition reaction—a reaction in which a single reactant breaks down to form two or more products (p. 7)

diffusion—the movement of particles from areas of higher concentration to areas of lower concentration (p. 59)

ecosystem—a group of populations and their nonliving environment (p. 68)

egg—the female sex cell (p. 49)

electric current—the rate at which the electrons pass a given point in a wire (p. 29)

electrical energy—the energy of moving electrons (p. 29)

electromagnetic waves—waves that can travel through matter and empty space (p. 29)

electron—a negatively-charged particle that makes up part of an atom (p. 29)

endocytosis—the process by which a cell membrane surrounds a particle and then brings it inside the cell (p. 59)

endoplasmic reticulum—organelle where many chemical reactions occur (p. 40)

energy—the ability to do work (p. 29)

evolution—the gradual change in a species over time (p. 79)

exocytosis—the process by which a cell releases a large particle (p. 59)

fertilization—the joining of an egg and sperm (p. 49)

fluid—a substance that can flow and take the shape of its container (p. 17)

force—a push or a pull (p. 17)

fossil—the remains of an organism that has been preserved in the earth (p. 79)

friction—the force that opposes motion between two surfaces that are in contact (p. 17)

gas giant—one of the four large, outer planets made mostly of gases (p. 101)

Golgi complex—organelle that packages proteins (p. 40)

half-life—the time it takes for half of the unstable atoms in a sample to decay (p. 79)

heat—the energy that is transferred between objects that are at different temperatures (p. 29)

heredity—the passing of traits from parents to offspring (p. 49)

homeostasis—the maintenance of a stable internal environment (p. 59)

homologous chromosomes—a pair of chromosomes with the same structure that contain hereditary information for the same traits (p. 49)

host—the organism that is harmed in a parasitic relationship (p. 68)

igneous rock—a rock that forms when hot, liquid rock cools and solidifies (p. 90)

kinetic energy—the energy an object has because of its motion (p. 29)

lysosome—organelle that digests food materials and destroys harmful particles (p. 40)

magma—hot, liquid rock (p. 90)

mass—the amount of matter in an object (p. 7)

mass extinction—a period of time in Earth's history when many species become extinct (p. 79)

matter—anything that has both volume and mass (p. 7)

mechanical weathering—the process where rocks break into smaller pieces without changing their chemical composition (p. 90)

meiosis—the process of cell division that forms sex cells, each of which has half the number of chromosomes as found in the parent cell (p. 49)

metamorphic rock—a rock in which the structure, texture, or composition of the rock has changed (p. 90)

mineral—a natural, solid substance that has a crystal structure (p. 90)

mitochondrion—organelle that produces energy (p. 40)

mitosis—the process of cell division that forms two nuclei that contain identical DNA (p. 49)

motion—the change in position of an object over time with respect to a reference point (p. 17)

multicellular—an organism that is made of more than one cell (p. 40)

mutualism—a symbiotic relationship in which both organisms benefit (p. 68)

net force—the combination of all the forces acting on an object (p. 17)

newton—the unit for force (p. 17)

niche—the role an organism plays in its environment (p. 68)

nucleus—organelle that directs much of the cell's processes (p. 40)

organ—a group of two or more tissues that work together to perform a specific job (p. 40)

organ system—a group of organs that work together to perform a specific job (p. 40)

organelle—a part that makes up a cell (p. 40)

organism—a living thing (p. 40)

osmosis—the diffusion of water through a semipermeable membrane (p. 59)

parallel circuit—an electric circuit where all the parts are joined side by side (p. 29)

parasite—the organism that benefits in a parasitic relationship (p. 68)

parasitism—a symbiotic relationship where one organism benefits and the other organism is harmed (p. 68)

passive transport—the movement of particles without the use of energy (p. 59)

period of revolution—the time it takes for an object to revolve around the sun once (p. 101)

period of rotation—the time it takes for an object to rotate once (p. 101)

photosynthesis—the process plants use to make food (p. 40)

physical change—a change that affects one or more physical properties of an object (p. 7)

physical property—property that can be observed or measured without changing the matter's identity (p. 7)

population—the members of a species that live in a particular area (p. 68)

potential energy—the energy an object has because of its position (p. 29)

predator—an organism that eats all or part of another organism (p. 68)

pressure—the amount of force exerted on a given area (p. 17)

prey—an organism that is killed and eaten by another organism (p. 68)

product—a substance that is formed in a chemical reaction (p. 7)

radiation—the transfer of heat energy by electromagnetic waves (p. 29)

reactant—a starting material in a chemical reaction (p. 7)

retrograde rotation—the clockwise spin of a planet as seen from above its North Pole (p. 101)

ribosome—organelle where proteins are made (p. 40)

rock—a natural substance made of one or more minerals (p. 90)

rock cycle—the series of events in which new rock forms from old rock (p. 90)

sedimentary rock—a rock that forms from layers of sediment that are compacted and cemented together (p. 90)

series circuit—an electric circuit where all the parts are connected to form a single loop (p. 29)

soil—a substance made up of loose, weathered rock and organic material (p. 90)

species—a group of organisms that can mate with one another to produce fertile offspring (p. 68)

sperm—the male sex cell (p. 49)

state of equilibrium—a condition where the concentrations of a substance remain equal (p. 59)

symbiosis—the relationship between two different organisms living in close association with each other (p. 68)

synthesis reaction—a reaction in which two or more reactants combine to form one product (p. 7)

temperature—a measure of the average kinetic energy of the particles in an object (p. 29)

thermal energy—the kinetic energy of all the moving particles in an object (p. 29)

tissue—a groups of cells that work together to perform a specific job (p. 40)

unicellular—an organism that is made of a single cell (p. 40)

voltage—the amount of energy electrons release as they flow through a wire (p. 29)

volume—the amount of space taken up, or occupied, by an object (p. 7)

weight—a measure of the force of gravity on the mass of an object (p. 7)

work—the use of a force that causes an object to move in the direction of the force (p. 29)

Answer Key

Assessment, pp. 5–6

1. A	**2.** C	**3.** C	**4.** B
5. D	**6.** B	**7.** D	**8.** B
9. B	**10.** C	**11.** B	**12.** D
13. A	**14.** C	**15.** C	**16.** D

Unit 1, Lesson 1

Review, p. 11

1. C	**2.** B	**3.** A
4. C	**5.** D	**6.** B

7. The melting point of a substance is a physical property because it can be determined without changing the identity of the substance.
8. A chemical equation shows the new substances (products) that are made.

Properties of Matter, p. 12

1. mass	**2.** weight	**3.** product
4. physical	**5.** reactant	**6.** chemical
7. equation		

Answer to question: its properties

Changes in Matter, p. 13

1. False. A *chemical* change produces a new substance.
2. True
3. True
4. False. The boiling point of a substance is an example of a *physical* property.
5. True
6. False. *Mass* is a physical property of an object that does not change no matter where the object is located in the universe.
7. True
8. True
9. False. In a chemical equation, the reactants are placed *before* the arrow.

Physical and Chemical Changes, p. 14

1. mass (or volume)
2. volume (or mass)
3. mass
4. volume
5. physical (or chemical)
6. chemical (or physical)
7. physical
8. physical change
9. chemical change
10. chemical reaction
11. chemical reaction
12. chemical equation
13. chemical equation
14. reactants
15. products

Experiment: Changes in Water, p. 16

Results and Analysis

1. physical change
2. The volume of the ice is greater than the volume of the water. This is seen when the ice expands and pushes off the aluminum cap from the bottle.
3. chemical change
4. Tiny gas bubbles appeared near the pencil points in the water. These gas bubbles were hydrogen and oxygen.

Conclusion

One possible conclusion is that water can undergo both a physical change and a chemical change.

Answer Key cont'd.

Unit 1, Lesson 2
Review, p. 22
1. D **2.** B **3.** D **4.** A **5.** B **6.** C
7. The forces are balanced, resulting in a net force of zero.

Net Forces, p. 23
1. 15 N; south
2. 2 N; down the driveway
3. 7 N; upward
4. Yes. The force being applied upward is greater than the downward force of gravity.
5. The object will move downward because the net force is 3 N in that direction.

Science Friction, p. 24
1. C **2.** B **3.** A **4.** D

Motions and Forces Crossword Puzzle, p. 25
Across
4. balanced
9. sinks
8. Archimedes
11. Bernoulli
Down
1. fluid
3. reference
5. newton
7. friction
2. net force
4. buoyancy
6. pressure
10. motion

Pressure, p. 26
1. 0.1 N/cm^2 **2.** 250 pascals
3. 100 pascals **4.** 10 newtons

Experiment: Reducing Friction, p. 28
Results and Analysis
The "hovercraft" should glide above the countertop on a cushion of air.

Conclusion
Creating a cushion of air reduces the friction and allows a hovercraft to move more easily.

Unit 1, Lesson 3
Review, p. 34
1. C **2.** A **3.** C **4.** D **5.** B **6.** C
7. Conduction involves the transfer of heat between two objects that are in contact. Convection involves the transfer of heat through the motion of particles within a liquid or gas.

Calculating Work, p. 35
1. 500 joules **2.** 225 joules
3. We both did the same amount of work (300 joules).
4. No work was done, as the bookcase did not move.

Energy, Temperature, and Heat, p. 36
1. f **2.** e **3.** a, i **4.** g **5.** h
6. b **7.** d **8.** c **9.** b **10.** a

Electric Circuits, p. 37
1. Bulb 2 will not light.
2. Bulbs 1 and 2 will not light.
3. No. Switch 4 must be closed for Bulb 1 to light. If Switch 4 is closed, then Bulb 3 will also light.
4. No. For Bulb 3 to be off, Switch 4 must be open. Opening Switch 4 will prevent Bulb 2 from lighting.
5. Yes. Opening Switch 4 will prevent all the bulbs from lighting as it prevents a complete circuit.

Answer Key cont'd.

Experiment: Using the Heat from the Sun, p. 39
Results and Analysis
1. The hot dog gets cooked from the sun's heat.
2. radiation   3. convection

Conclusion
One possible conclusion is that the heat from the sun can be used to cook foods, such as hot dogs.

Unit 2, Lesson 4
Review, p. 44
1. C   2. A   3. A   4. D
5. C   6. B
7. Many organisms are unicellular and therefore do not have tissues, organs, or organ systems.

Cell Structures and Functions, p. 45
1. d	2. f	3. g	4. b
5. h or b	6. i	7. j	8. c
9. a	10. a	11. d	12. b
13. c	14. e	15. h	16. j

The Black Reaction, p. 46
1. C   2. D   3. A   4. C

Experiment: Taking Out the Green, p. 48
Results and Analysis
1. Several different colors should separate on the paper.
2. As the alcohol moves up the filter, the green pigment is carried along. Various pigments separate as the alcohol continues to move up the paper.

Conclusion
Chlorophyll is not the only pigment in a green plant. However, chlorophyll must be the most abundant and therefore masks the other pigments.

Unit 2, Lesson 5
Review, p. 53
1. B   2. A   3. C   4. C
5. D   6. B
7. The fertilized egg would contain twice the number of chromosomes that it normally has. As a result, the fertilized egg would not develop.

The Cell Cycle, p. 54
1. interphase → mitosis → cytokinesis → interphase, etc.
2. Both cytokinesis and mitosis take about the same time.
3. interphase
4. The process is a cycle that goes around and therefore is best shown as a circle.
5. The nucleus divides to form two nuclei with identical DNA.
6. The cytoplasm divides into two equal halves.

Mitosis, p. 55
1. 6 chromosomes
2. 3 homologous pairs
3. 12 chromatids
4. 6 chromosomes
5. Mitosis produces cells that each has the identical DNA as the parent cell.

Answer Key cont'd.

The Sex Chromosomes, p. 56

1. A female cell contains a pair of sex chromosomes, both of which are X chromosomes. A male cell contains a pair of sex chromosomes that includes one X chromosome and one Y chromosome.
2. She discovered how the sex of an individual was determined.
3. The sperm contains either a Y chromosome or an X chromosome. The sex of an individual is determined by which of these two chromosomes is contained in the sperm.

Experiment: Growth and Mitosis, p. 58
Results and Analysis

1. The surface and interior have a greenish color.
2. The ammonia seeps or diffuses farther into the smaller cube.

Conclusion

The higher surface area to volume ratio allows a substance to seep deeper into a smaller cell. If a cell is too large, then substances may not reach all parts of the cell. If the substance is needed for a life function, then the cell may die.

Unit 2, Lesson 6
Review, p. 63

1. C	**2.** A	**3.** D	**4.** D
5. B	**6.** A	**7.** C	

8. Materials do not naturally move from an area of low concentration to an area of high concentration. Therefore, energy must be supplied for this process to occur.

The Big Eaters, p. 64

1. Macrophages are named "big eaters" because they ingest bacteria and other large particles.
2. The bacteria prevent the lysosomes in the macrophage from fusing with the vesicles that contain bacteria.
3. The bacteria are surrounded by a protective coating that makes it difficult for the macrophages to "eat" them by endocytosis.
4. The person would be more susceptible to diseases and infections.

Diffusion and Osmosis, p. 65

1. Water is in higher concentration on the left side so it will move by osmosis to the right side.
2. Food coloring is in higher concentration on the right side so it will move by diffusion to the left side.
3. The drawing should show equal numbers of water and food coloring particles on each side of the membrane.

Experiment: Diffusion and Osmosis, p. 67
Results and Analysis

The potato slice in the water is rigid. The potato slice in sugar is somewhat limp. The potato slice in salt is limp.

Conclusions

Water was in a higher concentration in the "water" cup so it moved by osmosis into the potato slice. This filled the potato cells with water making the slice feel rigid. Sugar was in a higher concentration in the "sugar" cup so it diffused into the potato while water moved

Answer Key cont'd.

out by osmosis. The loss of water made the potato slice limp. Salt was in a higher concentration in the "salt" cup so it diffused into the potato while water moved out by osmosis. The loss of water made the potato slice limp. Because the potato slice was limper in the salt water, this slice must have lost more water than the slice in the sugar water.

Unit 2, Lesson 7
Review, p. 72
1. D   2. A   3. B   4. C
5. B   6. A   7. D
8. If a parasite killed its host, it would have to find another one rather quickly to survive.
9. Answers will vary. Possible answers include a mockingbird/tree or a remora/shark described in the lesson.

Ecosystem Crossword Puzzle, p. 74
Across
3. host
10. adaptation
12. commensalism
13. ecosystem

5. population
11. niche

Down
1. camouflage
4. competition
7. predator
9. parasite

2. mutualism
6. species
8. symbiosis

The Termite—Is It a Pest or a Benefit?, p. 75
1. The termites and tiny organisms inside them exhibit mutualism. The tiny organisms provide food for the termites while the termites provide shelter for the microorganisms.
2. Termites can be both pests and provide benefits. They are pests when they destroy houses by eating wood. They provide a benefit in the desert by decomposing wastes.

A Striking Resemblance, p. 76
1. C   2. A   3. D

Experiment: Competition Among Plants, p. 78
Results and Analysis
1. Results will vary.   2. Results will vary.
Conclusion
Seeds that have more space to germinate and grow will produce taller plants. Seeds that have less space compete for the limited resources and therefore cannot grow as tall.

Unit 2, Lesson 8
Review, p. 83
1. B   2. C   3. D   4. A   5. D   6. C
7. A common ancestor is an organism from which two different organisms evolved.
8. For the most part, humans have had a negative impact on biodiversity by destroying, polluting, and altering the environment.

Pangea, p. 84
1. South America, Africa, Asia, and Australia
2. South America, Africa, and Antarctica
3. Yes. Fossil of both organisms have been found on at least two continents (South America and Africa) separated by an

Answer Key cont'd.

ocean. This suggests that these two continents were once connected.

Fossils and Rock Layers, p. 85
1. The number of herbivores decreased.
2. The number of carnivores increased.
3. Possible answers include that more and more herbivores were eaten by carnivores, that less light was available for photosynthesis, and that herbivores lacked adaptations needed to survive their changing environment.
4. Possible answers include that the number of carnivores increased because more food became available, and that carnivores possessed adaptations to survive their changing environment.

Identifying an Organism, p. 86
(a) English oak
(b) shingle oak
(c) Lombardy poplar
(d) live oak
(e) redbud
(f) chestnut oak

A Chinese Treasure, p. 87
1. B   2. C   3. D

Experiment: Half-Life, p. 89
Results and Analysis
1. an unstable atom that decays
2. a half-life
3. about 50 percent
Conclusion
Pennies can serve as a model of a half-life because the pennies that land heads up represent atoms that have decayed.

Unit 3, Lesson 9
Review, p. 94
1. B   2. C   3. A   4. B   5. D   6. C
7. Metamorphic rock is formed by intense heat and pressure which are likely to destroy any fossils.

The Rock Cycle, p. 95
1. heat and pressure
2. weathering and erosion
3. A metamorphic rock can change into a different kind of metamorphic rock.
4. Deposition is the process by which sediments form layers.
5. Uplift is the process by which rocks are brought from under the ground to the Earth's surface.

The Composition of a Rock, p. 96
1. orthoclase 30%; plagioclase 20%; biotite 10%; quartz 40%
2. 4 grams of quartz and 1 gram of biotite
3. This graph does not support this statement as it shows quartz as the most common mineral.
4. 50%

Chemical Weathering, p. 97
1. location 5 because it receives the most rainfall and therefore the most potential acid precipitation
2. location 4 because it receives the least amount of rainfall
3. There is no information provided to make any definite statements about mechanical weathering at these locations. However,

Answer Key
Science 6, SV 9781419034343

Answer Key cont'd.

one can predict that the more rainfall there is, the more erosion will occur. Erosion is a cause of mechanical weathering. Therefore, location 5 would have the most mechanical weathering.

Experiment: Acid Precipitation, p. 100
Results and Analysis
1. The pH became less acidic as the limestone neutralized the acidity of the vinegar/water mixture.
2. The pH did not change.
Conclusion
Limestone can be used to neutralize the effects of acid precipitation.

Unit 3, Lesson 10
Review, p. 105
1. C 2. A 3. D 4. C 5. A 6. B
7. 186,000 miles/second $\times$ 30 seconds = 5,580,000 miles
8. You can determine the relative periods of revolution and their average surface temperatures.
9. A planet cannot cross the orbit of another celestial body as it travels around the sun. Pluto's orbit crosses that of Neptune, so it has been reclassified as a "dwarf planet."

The Inner Planets, p. 106
1. Earth, Venus, Mars, Mercury
2. No. For example, Mercury has the shortest period of revolution and the second longest period of rotation.
3. 93,000,000 miles $\times$ 0.72 = about 67,000,000 miles
4. 1.5 AU $\times$ 8.3 light-minutes/AU = 12.45 light-minutes
5. 88 days/58 days = about 1.5 times

The Outer Planets, p. 107
1. Neptune, Uranus, Saturn, Jupiter
2. 93 million miles $\times$ 30.1 = 2,799,300,000 miles
3. 79.68 light-minutes, or 1 light-hour and 19.68 light-minutes
4. 2.656 light-hours
5. about 15 times

Comparing Planets, p. 108
1. Neptune and Uranus have about the same volume, while Earth has a significantly smaller volume.
2. Uranus has a mass about 14 times that of Earth's, while Neptune has a mass about 18 times that of Earth's.
3. Density depends not only on mass but also on volume. Earth has much more mass per unit volume, or density, than either Uranus or Neptune.

Answer Key cont'd.

Naming a Planet, p. 109

1. Uranus is the "grandfather" of Pluto, Jupiter, and Neptune.
2. Tradition holds that planets and other celestial objects are named after Greek and Roman gods and goddesses.
3. No. Other scientists came up with the name for Uranus, while a girl suggested Pluto's name.

Experiment: Density, p. 111

Results and Analysis
The bowling ball should float.
Conclusion
Because it floats, the bowling ball must be less dense than water.

4500742773-0607-2018

Printed in the U.S.A